Illustrations Credits

All illustrations © K12 Inc. unless otherwise noted

Elephant. © Photodisc/Getty Images
Water buffalo. © Dynamic Graphics/Jupiterimages
Elk. © Photos.com/Jupiterimages
Moose. © liquidlibrary/Thinkstock
Bison. © Jupiterimages
Polar bear. © Warren Jacobi/Corbis
Black bear. © Photodisc/Getty Images
Giraffe. © Photos.com/Jupiterimages

About K12 Inc.

K12 Inc., a technology-based education company, is the nation's leading provider of proprietary curriculum and online education programs to students in grades K–12. K12 provides its curriculum and academic services to online schools, traditional classrooms, blended school programs, and directly to families. K12 Inc. also operates the K12 International Academy, an accredited, diploma-granting online private school serving students worldwide. K12's mission is to provide any child the curriculum and tools to maximize success in life, regardless of geographic, financial, or demographic circumstances. K12 Inc. is accredited by CITA. More information can be found at www.K12.com.

ISBN: 978-1-60153-083-7
Printed by RR Donnelley & Sons, Roanoke, VA, USA, April 2013, Lot 040513

Contents

Whole Number Sense

Whole Number Addition and Subtraction

Algebra Thinking

Whole Number Multiplication Sense

Whole Number Multiplication

Whole Number Division Sense

Whole Number Division

Whole Numbers and Multiple Operations

Geometry

Decimals and Money

Measurement: Length and Time

Measurement: Capacity and Weight

Mathematical Reasoning

2008 2004
2001

Worked Examples

You can count to find missing numbers.

PROBLEM What's the next number?

4,545   4,546   4,547   ?

SOLUTION To find the next number, count up 1 from the previous number. So 4,547 and 1 more is 4,548.

ANSWER 4,548

Count by ones. What's the missing number?

1. 1,074   1,075   1,076   ?
   A. 1,077   B. 1,070   C. 1,770

2. 6,004   6,005   ?   6,007
   A. 6,006   B. 6,008   C. 6,060

3. 2,897   2,898   2,899   ?
   A. 2,896   B. 2,999   C. 2,900

4. 7,108   7,109   ?   7,111   7,112
   A. 7,100   B. 7,110   C. 7,113

LEARN

5. 3,998   3,999   ?   4,001   4,002   4,003

A. 4,004   B. 4,100   C. 4,000

6. 9,996   9,997   9,998   9,999   ?

A. 10,000   B. 1,000   C. 1,001

7. 8,998   8,999   9,000   ?   9,002

A. 9,110   B. 9,001   C. 9,010

8. 5,459   ?   5,461   5,462   5,463

A. 5,458   B. 5,464   C. 5,460

9. 6,998   6,999   7,000   ?

A. 7,001   B. 7,101   C. 7,110

LEARN

Numbers Through 10,000

Numerals Through 10,000

Use the place-value chart to answer Problems 1–4.
Complete each sentence. Write *thousands, hundreds, tens,* or *ones.*

Thousands						
hundred thousands	ten thousands	thousands		hundreds	tens	ones
		3	,	4	6	2

1. The 6 is in the __?__ place.

2. The 2 is in the __?__ place.

3. The 4 is in the __?__ place.

4. The 3 is in the __?__ place.

Start at the following numbers. Count aloud the next 10 numbers.

5. 994

6. 1,055

7. 8,199

8. 6,998

Use the beads to answer Problems 9–12.

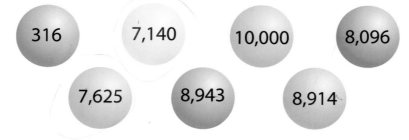

9. Which numbers have a 7 in the thousands place?

10. Which numbers have a 9 in the hundreds place?

11. Which number has a 1 in the ten thousands place?

12. Which numbers have a 6 in the ones place?

T R Y   I T

Answer the question.

13. What is the value of the underlined digit? 6,2<u>3</u>9

14. What is the value of the underlined digit? <u>1</u>,582

15. Which digit is in the hundreds place in 1,492?

Choose the answer.

16. Which **two** numbers have a 9 in both the tens place and the thousands place?

    A. 9,890   B. 9,109   C. 3,999   D. 9,295

17. Which is the value of the 2 in the number 2,856?

A.   B.   C. | | D. ▪▪

18. Which is the value of the 2 in the number 5,0<u>2</u>3?

A. 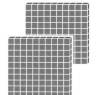   B.   C. | | D. ▪▪

Odd and Even Numbers

Odd or Even?

For Problem 1, use the large numbers shown.

1. Draw a square. In that square, write all the even numbers shown here.

    Draw a triangle. In that triangle, write all the odd numbers shown here.

39   34   323

46   948

    721   1,000

64   171   563

Choose the answer.

2. Which of these collections can be evenly divided between two people?

    A. 600 pennies   B. 43 balloons

3. Which of these groups can be evenly divided between two people?

    A. 86 grapes   B. 937 crayons

TRY IT

Write the answer.

4. Write an even number that is between 667 and 671.

5. What is the greatest odd number less than 92?

6. What is the greatest even number less than 63?

7. Write the odd numbers between 699 and 708.

8. Write the even numbers between 199 and 209.

9. Sammy said that when he added two even numbers, he always got an odd number. Is this always true? Write three examples to help explain your answer.

10. Explain two ways to figure out if a number is even.

Choose the answer.

11. Which of these numbers is an odd number?
    A. 766   B. 867   C. 894   D. 900

12. Which of these numbers is an even number?
    A. 544   B. 655   C. 761   D. 873

13. Which number line shows only odd numbers?

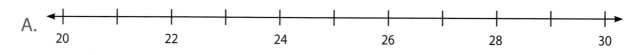

A.
20   22   24   26   28   30

B.
71   73   75   77   79   81

14. If you added the odd numbers 3,237 and 2,461, would the sum be odd or even?
    A. even   B. odd

TRY IT

Choose the answer.

15. Andre and Ben both have an odd number of baseballs. Andre buys 2 more baseballs and Ben buys 5 more baseballs. Which statement is true?

    A. Andre now has an even number of baseballs and Ben now has an even number of baseballs.

    B. Andre now has an odd number of baseballs and Ben now has an odd number of baseballs.

    C. Andre now has an even number of baseballs and Ben now has an odd number of baseballs.

    D. Andre now has an odd number of baseballs and Ben now has an even number of baseballs.

TRY IT

Write and Read Numerals

Read aloud the number.

1. 6,291

2. 10,000

3. 586

4. 9,360

5. 2,074

6. 5,109

7. 3,042

8. 1,423

9. 4,240

10. 8,508

11. 3,200

12. 1,070

13. 4,002

14. 10,000

15. 9,387

TRY IT

Write the number.

16. two thousand, thirty

17. ten thousand

Choose the answer.

18. Which is the correct way to write six thousand, four hundred eighty-three?

    A. 6,483   B. 6,384   C. 6,843   D. 6,438

19. Jilly wrote three thousand, seven hundred three. Which is Jilly's number?

    A. 3,703   B. 3,730   C. 3,307   D. 3,700

20. Helen wrote four thousand, one. Which is Helen's number?

    A. 4,010   B. 4,001   C. 4,110   D. 4,100

T R Y   I T

Write Number Words Through 10,000

Write Number Words

Write the number word.

1. 8,912

2. 7,990

3. 4,800

4. 10,000

Choose the number word.

5. 5,675
   - A. five thousand, six hundred seventy-five
   - B. fifty thousand, six hundred seventy-five
   - C. five thousand, six hundred fifty-seven
   - D. five thousand, seventy-five

6. 2,989
   - A. twenty thousand, nine hundred eighty-nine
   - B. two thousand, ninety-eight hundred
   - C. two thousand, nine hundred eighty-nine
   - D. two thousand, eighty-nine

TRY IT

At the zoo, Johnny saw eight large animals. He made a chart and wrote each animal's weight. Write the number words for each weight.

Weight of Animals at the Zoo		
Animal	**Weight (in pounds)**	**Number words**
7. Elephant	9,456	?
8. Water buffalo	2,630	?
9. Elk	873	?
10. Moose	1,052	?
11. Bison	2,109	?

TRY IT

Weight of Animals at the Zoo		
Animal	Weight (in pounds)	Number words
12. Polar bear	1,314	?
13. Black bear	527	?
14. Giraffe	3,800	?

Numbers in Expanded Form

Expanded Form and Standard Form

Memory Jogger

STANDARD FORM AND EXPANDED FORM

STANDARD FORM is the way we usually write numbers.

Example: 422 or 7,005

EXPANDED FORM is a way of writing numbers that shows the place value of each number. We can write numbers in expanded form two ways.

1 With numbers and words: $422 = 4 \text{ hundreds} + 2 \text{ tens} + 2 \text{ ones}$

2 With numbers only: $422 = 400 + 20 + 2$

When a number has a zero in one or more places, those places are not shown in the expanded form.

Example: $7,005 = 7 \text{ thousands} + 5 \text{ ones}$
$7,005 = 7,000 + 5$

Write the number in expanded form with numbers only.

1. 2,964

2. 7,419

3. 3,620

4. 8,904

5. 5,046

6. 9,007

Choose the answer.

7. Which shows 6,430 written in expanded form?

A. $6,000 + 400 + 30$

B. $6 + 4 + 3$

C. $6,000 + 40 + 3$

D. $600 + 40 + 30$

TRY IT

8. Which means the same as 4,602?

    A. 4 thousands + 6 hundreds + 2 ones

    B. 4 hundreds + 6 thousands + 2 ones

    C. 4 thousands + 6 ones + 2 hundreds

    D. 4 thousands + 6 tens + 2 ones

9. Jim counted the number of jelly beans in a container.
He counted 4,000 black, 30 pink, 900 purple, and 1 red.
How many jelly beans are in the container?

    A. 4,931   B. 4,391

    C. 4,193   D. 4,139

Complete the table. Write the missing standard form or expanded form of the number.

	Standard form	Expanded form with numbers only	Expanded form with numbers and words
10.	9,394	9,000 + 300 + 90 + 4	?
11.	203	200 + 3	?
12.	5,043	5,000 + 40 + 3	?
13.	1,124	?	1 thousand + 1 hundred + 2 tens + 4 ones
14.	6,599	?	6 thousands + 5 hundreds + 9 tens + 9 ones
15.	2,207	?	2 thousands + 2 hundreds + 7 ones
16.	?	1,000 + 70 + 7	1 thousand + 7 tens + 7 ones
17.	?	500 + 7	5 hundreds + 7 ones

TRY IT

Construct Numbers to 10,000 (A)

Place Value as Multiples of 10

You can use blocks and a chart to show numbers in different ways.

PROBLEM The number 325 can be shown as 3 hundreds, 2 tens, and 5 ones. Show 325 with base-10 blocks at least three other ways. Record your answers in a chart.

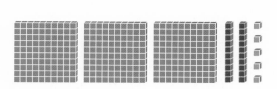

325		
hundreds	tens	ones
3	2	5

SOLUTION You can show the number many different ways. Here are a few examples.

1 Regroup 1 hundred into 10 tens.

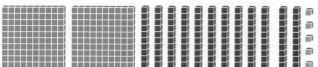

2	12	5

2 Regroup 1 hundred into 10 tens.
Regroup 1 ten into 10 ones.

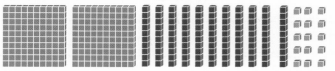

2	11	15

L E A R N

3 Regroup 3 hundreds into 30 tens.
Regroup 2 tens into 20 ones.

325		
hundreds	tens	ones
	30	25

4 Regroup hundreds and tens into ones.

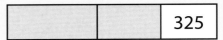

		325

ANSWER

325		
hundreds	tens	ones
3	2	5
2	12	5
2	11	15
	30	25
		325

LEARN

Use base-10 blocks to complete each problem.

1. Show the number 453 with base-10 blocks
   five different ways. Record each way.
   The first answer is shown.

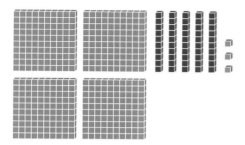

453		
hundreds	tens	ones
4	5	3
?	?	?
?	?	?
	?	?
		?

2. Show the number 1,546 with base-10 blocks
   four different ways. Record each way.
   The first answer is shown.

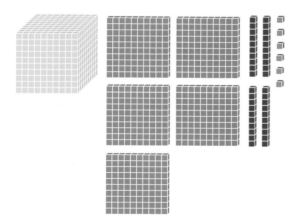

1,546			
thousands	hundreds	tens	ones
1	5	4	6
	?	?	?
	?	?	?
?	?	?	?

L E A R N

3. In the chart, show how to make the number 10,000 using only hundreds, only tens, and only ones.

10,000				
ten thousands	thousands	hundreds	tens	ones
1				
	10			
	9	10		
		?		
			?	
				?

LEARN

Worked Examples

You can write a number in standard form for any combination of base-10 blocks. (Reminder: Standard form is the way we normally write numbers.)

PROBLEM What is the standard form of the number we can make with 23 tens rods and 5 ones cubes?

SOLUTION

1. Look at how many ones and tens there are.

2. If there are more than 10 of any kind of block, regroup to make one or more blocks of the next greater place value.

3. There are 23 tens rods and 5 ones cubes.
   Regroup 20 tens so there are 2 hundreds, 3 tens and 5 ones.

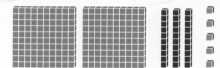

4. Write the answer in standard form—235.

ANSWER 235

Write the standard form for each number.

4. 40 tens and 8 ones

5. 27 tens

6. 12 hundreds and 25 ones

7. 3 thousands, 15 hundreds, 1 ten, and 32 ones

LEARN

Construct Numbers to 10,000 (A)

Working with Place Value

Use base-10 blocks to complete each problem.

1. Fill in the blank. 832 can be shown with 8 hundreds flats, 2 tens rods, and ___?___ ones cubes.

2. Show 220 using only tens rods.

3. Show 1,400 using only hundreds flats.

4. What is another name for 78 tens?

5. Show the number 364 three different ways with blocks and in a chart.

364		
hundreds	**tens**	**ones**
?	?	?
?	?	?
?	?	?

6. Show the number 1,246 using the fewest number of base-10 blocks.

TRY IT

7. Susan organized her paper clips into trays of hundreds, tens, and ones. She had 2 groups of 100 paper clips, 9 groups of 10 paper clips, and 5 single paper clips. She gets 16 more paper clips. Explain how she could regroup her paper clips so that she still has them in hundreds, tens, and ones.

8. Tom shows the number 759 with base-10 blocks. He uses 6 hundreds flats. Show how many tens and ones he will need.

Choose the answer.

9. Kim arranged her seashells in groups of 10. She counted and found that she had 16 groups of 10 seashells. Which is another way to write how many seashells Kim has?

   A. 10   B. 16

   C. 160   D. 163

TRY IT

Construct Numbers to 10,000 (B)

Constructing Numbers to 10,000

Use base-10 blocks for Problems 1–3. Record how many of each block you use.

1. Show the number 923 three different ways.

2. Matt shows the number 258. He uses 24 tens. Show how many ones he will need.

3. Ashley shows the number 593. She uses 23 ones. Show how many hundreds and tens she will need.

You may use base-10 blocks to help you answer Problems 4–6.

4. Write 6 hundreds, 12 tens, and 14 ones in standard form. Explain the trades needed to write the number in standard form.

5. Explain why 573 is the same as 4 hundreds, 17 tens, and 3 ones.

6. Explain why 304 is the same as 2 hundreds, 8 tens, and 24 ones.

TRY IT

Round Numbers Through 10,000

Round to Tens, Hundreds, and Thousands

Look at the number line for each problem. Choose the answer.

1. Which number is the nearest ten to 84?

A. 80   B. 90

2. Which number is the nearest ten to 123?

A. 120   B. 130

3. Which number is the nearest hundred to 472?

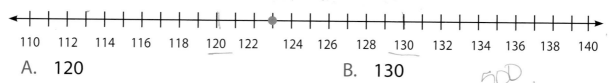

A. 400   B. 500

4. Which number is the nearest hundred to 2,356?

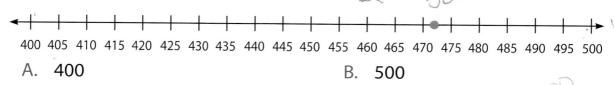

A. 2,300   B. 2,400

5. Which number is the nearest thousand to 5,701?

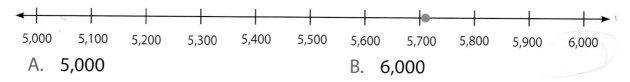

A. 5,000   B. 6,000

TRY IT

Write the answer.

6. If you want to round 3,483 to the nearest thousand, what are the boundary numbers?

3,483

2,000   3,000   4,000   5,000

7. Round 3,483 to the nearest thousand.

8. Round 4,654 to the nearest hundred.

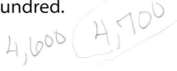

4,600 (4,700)

Choose the answer.

9. Michael wants to round 809 to the nearest hundred. Which boundary numbers should he use?

   A. 800 and 810   B. 800 and 900

   C. 800 and 1,000   D. 700 and 800

10. Dawn says 14 rounded to the nearest ten is 10. Eddie says 14 rounded to the nearest ten is 0. Who is correct? Why?

   A. Dawn is correct because the ten nearest to 14 is 10.

   B. Eddie is correct because 14 is closer to 0 than to 20.

11. Which shows 4,008 rounded to the nearest thousand?

   A. 4,010   B. 4,100   C. 4,000   D. 5,000

12. Which shows 2,132 rounded to the nearest ten?

   A. 2,100   B. 2,130   C. 2,140   D. 2,200

13. Which shows 6,781 rounded to the nearest hundred?

   A. 6,500   B. 6,700   C. 6,800   D. 6,900

14. Which shows 7,651 rounded to the nearest thousand?

   A. 7,000   B. 7,600   C. 7,700   D. 8,000

TRY IT

Write the answer.

15. Gina wants to round 6,726 to the nearest ten.
Explain how she should do it.

16. Explain how to round 4,522 to the nearest thousand.

17. Lila says that 3,772 rounded to the nearest hundred is
3,700. Is Lila correct? Explain why or why not.

18. Calvin rounded the number 2,345 to the nearest
hundred. He said the answer was 2,400. Calvin explained
that he figured out that 2,345 was closer to 2,350.
Then he said 2,350 was closer to 2,400 than 2,300.
Did Calvin correctly round 2,345 to the nearest hundred?

TRY IT

Addition and Subtraction Answers

Add Numbers Through 10,000

Add.

1. $\begin{array}{r} 3{,}291 \\ +\ 5{,}947 \\ \hline \end{array}$

2. $\begin{array}{r} 2{,}117 \\ 3{,}123 \\ +\ 3{,}852 \\ \hline \end{array}$

3. $\begin{array}{r} 2{,}664 \\ +\ 7{,}336 \\ \hline \end{array}$

4. $\begin{array}{r} 1{,}553 \\ +\ 8{,}447 \\ \hline \end{array}$

5. $\begin{array}{r} 7{,}825 \\ +\ 1{,}287 \\ \hline \end{array}$

6. $4{,}696 + 3{,}754 = \underline{\ ?\ }$

7. $2{,}809 + 3{,}476 = \underline{\ ?\ }$

8. $\underline{\ ?\ } = 5{,}869 + 4{,}131$

Choose the answer.

9. $\begin{array}{r} 3{,}892 \\ +\ 5{,}708 \\ \hline \end{array}$

   A. 8,500
   B. 8,590
   C. 9,500
   D. 9,600

10. $4{,}816 + 1{,}794 = \underline{\ ?\ }$

    A. 3,022
    B. 3,182
    C. 5,610
    D. 6,610

TRY IT

Addition and Subtraction Answers

Subtract Numbers Through 10,000

Subtract.

1. $$\begin{array}{r} 9,714 \\ -\ 2,337 \\ \hline \end{array}$$

2. $$\begin{array}{r} 5,025 \\ -\ 4,261 \\ \hline \end{array}$$

3. $$\begin{array}{r} 10,000 \\ -\ 7,836 \\ \hline \end{array}$$

4. $$\begin{array}{r} 10,000 \\ -\ 3,561 \\ \hline \end{array}$$

5. $$\begin{array}{r} 1,044 \\ -\ \ \ 88 \\ \hline \end{array}$$

6. $6,599 - 1,570 = \underline{\ ?\ }$

7. $5,281 - 3,004 = \underline{\ ?\ }$

8. $9,925 - 1,475 = \underline{\ ?\ }$

Choose the answer.

9. $7,562 - 1,516 = \underline{\ ?\ }$

   A. 6,046

   B. 6,054

   C. 8,078

   D. 9,078

10. $$\begin{array}{r} 4,563 \\ -\ \ 856 \\ \hline \end{array}$$

   A. 3,507

   B. 3,707

   C. 4,419

   D. 5,419

TRY IT

Compare and Equalize Story Problems

Compare and Solve

Read the problem. Answer the question.

1. 2,043 people drove to the football game. 3,102 people took a bus or a train to the game. How many more people took a bus or train to the game?

3,102	
2,043	?

Write the number sentence you can use to solve the problem, and then solve.

2. The soccer stadium has 5,645 seats. It has 3,425 fewer seats than the football stadium. How many seats does the football stadium have?

FB 5,645
P 5,645 + 3,425

Choose the number sentence that could be used to solve the problem.

3. Ella collected 2,345 pennies. Linda has 234 more pennies than Ella. How many pennies does Linda have?

   A. $2,345 - 234 = \square$ B. $2,345 + 234 = \square$ C. $234 - 2,345 = \square$

TRY IT

Compare and Equalize Story Problems

Make Equal Amounts

Read the problem. Write the number sentence
and the solution to the problem.

1. There are 1,923 pumpkin seeds. There are 3,997 watermelon
    seeds. How many more pumpkin seeds do you need if you
    want to have the same amount as the watermelon seeds?

    Number sentence: _?_

    Solution: _?_

2. Farmer Li has 2,457 pounds of green beans. He has 1,032 pounds
    of peas. How many pounds of green beans would he have to sell
    to have the same amount of green beans and peas?

    Number sentence: _?_

    Solution: _?_

Choose the number sentence that could be used
to solve this problem.

3. The City Art Gallery has 3,458 paintings in its collection. If
    it buys 1,257 more paintings, it will have as many paintings
    as the National Art Gallery. How many paintings does the
    National Art Gallery have?

    A. $1,257 - 3,458 = \square$

    B. $3,458 - 1,257 = \square$

    C. $3,458 + 1,257 = \square$

TRY IT

Mathematical Expressions

Story Expressions

Worked Examples

You can change story problem situations into expressions. Write an expression for each story.

PROBLEM 1 Rosa has 3 tickets. She buys 5 more.

SOLUTION Think about the story and change it into an expression by writing it as numbers and operation symbols ($+$, $-$, $\times$, $\div$).

Rosa has 3 tickets. She buys 5 more. Rosa starts with 3 and then buys more, so add the two amounts.

ANSWER $3 + 5$

PROBLEM 2 Rosa had 8 tickets. She gave 3 away.

ANSWER $8 - 3$

PROBLEM 3 Rosa has 3 tickets. Maria has twice as many.

ANSWER 2×3

PROBLEM 4 Rosa has 12 tickets. She puts them in 3 equal groups.

ANSWER $12 \div 3$

Write an expression to show the story problem situation.

1. Rosa goes to the carnival with $15. She spends $10 on tickets.

2. Rosa has 6 stuffed bears. She wins 5 more.

3. There are 7 candy apples. There are twice as many funnel cakes.

4. Rosa buys 18 balloons and divides them into 2 equal groups.

5. Rosa had 12 tickets. She has 8 fewer tickets after riding the carousel.

6. There are 4 ponies at the carnival. There are twice as many cows.

7. There are 10 girls on the Ferris wheel. There are twice as many boys.

8. Rosa buys 20 tickets. She shares them equally with her friend.

Look at the expression on the ticket. Choose the word or phrase that completes the story to match the expression.

9. Sara has 24 tickets. Then she _?_ 6 more.

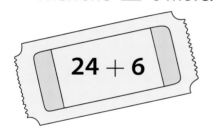

$$24 + 6$$

A. buys

B. sells

10. Jake has 3 tickets. Mark has 5 _?_ tickets.

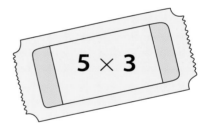

$$5 \times 3$$

A. times as many

B. more

11. Bryan has 8 tickets. He _?_ 6.

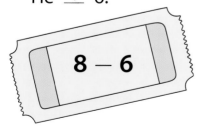

$$8 - 6$$

A. buys

B. gives away

12. Caden buys 10 tickets. He _?_ .

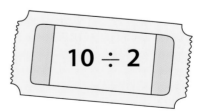

$$10 \div 2$$

A. puts them in 2 equal groups

B. uses 2 tickets to buy cotton candy

LEARN

Mathematical Expressions

Identify and Write Expressions

Choose the answer.

1. Which expression shows 5 more than 15?

   A. $15 + 5$ B. 15×5

   C. $5 - 5$ D. $15 \div 5$

2. Which expression shows 10 divided into 2 equal groups?

   A. $10 + 2$ B. 10×2

   C. $10 - 2$ D. $10 \div 2$

3. Which expression shows 4 less than 9?

   A. $9 + 4$ B. 9×4

   C. $9 - 4$ D. $9 \div 4$

4. Which expression shows twice as many as 3?

   A. $2 + 3$ B. 2×3

   C. $2 - 3$ D. $2 \div 3$

5. Tom washed 8 cars and then he washed 14 more. Which expression shows how many cars he washed in all?

   A. $8 + 14$ B. $14 \div 8$ C. 8×14 D. $8 - 14$

Write the expression.

6. 7 more than 15

7. 8 less than 21

8. 10 times 4

9. Gavin has 13 toy trucks. He buys 5 more.

10. Jane planted 25 tulips. She picks 15 of the tulips.

11. Will had $18. He spent $3.

12. Valeria has 7 boxes. Each box has 2 shoes.

13. Dina has 20 bananas. She divides them equally among 10 friends.

TRY IT

Expressions and Number Sentences (A)

Equal Expressions

Write the expression.

1. Write five expressions equal to $20 - 4$.
   Use different operations in your expressions.

Match each expression on the left with an equal expression on the right. Then write a number sentence for each pair.

2. $35 - 5$ A. $6 + 6$

3. $7 + 7$ B. $2 + 18$

4. 20×1 C. $14 - 0$

5. $10 + 2$ D. $0 + 5$

6. $6 - 1$ E. 6×5

Choose the number sentence that could be used to solve the problem.

7. The construction team built a house with 15 square windows and 4 round windows. How many windows were there in all?

   A. $15 \div 4 = \square$ B. $15 \times 4 = \square$

   C. $15 + 4 = \square$ D. $15 - 4 = \square$

8. Stripes the dog had 18 dog biscuits. He ate 4 biscuits in the morning and 7 in the afternoon. How many dog biscuits does he have left?

   A. $18 + 7 - 4 = \square$ B. $18 - 4 - 7 = \square$

   C. $7 + 18 - 4 = \square$ D. $4 + 18 - 7 = \square$

T R Y   I T

Write a number sentence that could be used to solve the problem.

9. After a race, 9 runners each drank 2 cups of water. How many cups of water did they drink altogether?

10. Tennis headbands cost $2 each. How many headbands can you buy for $30?

TRY IT

Expressions and Number Sentences (B)

Choose the Number Sentence

Choose the number sentence that represents the problem.

1. Candy Apple Café sells candy apples at the carnival. On Friday, 120 candy apples were sold. On Saturday, 60 candy apples were sold. How many total candy apples were sold on those two days?

   A. $\square = 120 + 60$

   B. $\square = 120 - 60$

   C. $120 \div 60 = \square$

2. The clowns are putting on a show at the carnival. There are 50 people watching the show. Before the show is over, 12 people leave and 9 people arrive. How many people are now watching the show?

   A. $\square = 50 + 12 + 9$

   B. $\square = 50 - 12 - 9$

   C. $\square = 50 - 12 + 9$

3. Candy apples cost $4 each. Jerome and his friends want to buy 8 candy apples. How much money do they need?

   A. $\square = 4 + 8$

   B. $\square = 4 \times 8$

   C. $\square = 8 \div 4$

4. There are 20 people riding the roller coaster. They are in 5 cars, and an equal number of people are in each car. How many people are in each car?

   A. $20 \div 5 = \square$

   B. $20 \times 5 = \square$

   C. $20 + 5 = \square$

   D. $20 - 5 = \square$

TRY IT

5. Paula read 5 pages of her book each hour for 3 hours. How many pages did she read in all?

   A. $5 + 3 = \square$ B. $5 \times 3 = \square$

   C. $5 \div 3 = \square$ D. $5 - 3 = \square$

6. Dario had $30. He spent $12 at the toy store and $10 at the paper store. How much money does he have left?

   A. $\$30 + \$12 + \$10 = \square$ B. $\$30 + \$12 - \$10 = \square$

   C. $\$12 + \$30 - \$10 = \square$ D. $\$30 - \$12 - \$10 = \square$

7. Sasha had 43 table tennis balls. She lost 22 of them and then found 12. How many balls does she have now?

   A. $43 + 22 + 12 = \square$ B. $43 - 22 - 12 = \square$

   C. $43 + 22 - 12 = \square$ D. $43 - 22 + 12 = \square$

Write a number sentence that could be used to solve the problem.

8. Kelly read 250 pages on Saturday and 50 pages on Sunday. How many pages did Kelly read on these two days?

9. The bakery baked 35 loaves of bread. Of the loaves, 18 were white. The rest were wheat. How many loaves were wheat?

10. The gazelle spends 12 hours a day grazing for food. How many hours would the gazelle spend grazing in 5 days?

TRY IT

Expression Comparison (A)

Represent Situations

Compare the expressions on each balloon.
Write the symbol ($<$, $>$, $=$) that makes the
number sentence true.

$10 + 8 \boxed{>} 16$

1.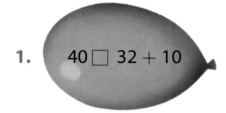

   $40 \square 32 + 10$

2. $18 \square 28 - 10$

3. $20 + 6 \square 20 + 7$

4.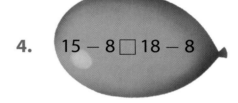

   $15 - 8 \square 18 - 8$

Write an expression to represent the story problem.

5. Bobby has 12 tickets and
   he uses 8.

6. Tiana pops 3 balloons on
   each of 3 targets.

7. The class bought 14 vanilla
   cones and 9 chocolate cones.

8. Maria has 12 tickets and divides
   them into 2 equal groups.

TRY IT

Expression Comparison (B)

Compare Quantities

Worked Examples

You can use the $<$, $>$, or $=$ symbol to write a number sentence that compares quantities in story problems.

PROBLEM There are 4 racks with 3 pretzels on each rack. There is a bag of 8 pretzels.

SOLUTION

1 Break the situation into parts that can be written as expressions.

2 Decide if the first expression is less than, greater than, or equal to the second expression.

3 Compare the expressions with $<$, $>$, or $=$.

Expression 1:
4 racks with 3 pretzels on each rack
4×3

THINK:
$4 \times 3 = 12$

Expression 2:
bag of 8 pretzels
8

ANSWER

Number sentence:
$4 \times 3 > 8$

Write an expression to match the situation. Then write a number sentence to compare the numbers that are in the expression.

1. Mr. Weaver has 25 peanuts and gives the same number of peanuts to each of his 5 children. Mrs. Mead has 4 peanuts.

Expression 1:
25 peanuts to each of 5 children

25 ☐ 5

Think:
25 ☐ 5 = 5

Expression 2:
? peanuts

?

Number sentence:
?

2. Lola has 10 rings. Kari has 2 rings on each of 5 fingers.

Expression 1:
? rings

Expression 2:
? rings on each of ? fingers

Think:
?

Number sentence:
?

Write a number sentence to compare the numbers that are in the situation.

3. There are 45 children in the red line and 23 in the blue line for the roller coaster. There are 62 children in line for the fun house.

4. There are 72 prizes at the duck booth, and 49 prizes are given away. There are 56 prizes at the bottle booth.

5. There are 3 riders on the swings. On the cars there are 30 riders separated equally into 5 groups.

6. Each of 5 children tosses 3 rings. Mike tosses 8 rings.

7. There are 22 candy apples, and 18 are eaten. Seven children buy drinks.

8. Naomi plays games for 45 minutes. Allie plays skee ball for 10 minutes and ring toss for 20 minutes.

L E A R N

Expression Comparison (B)

Write Expressions

Write an expression to match the situation.
Then write a number sentence to compare the quantities.

1. There are 27 children on the train ride, and 9 get off the train.
    There are 16 children on the wagon ride.

    Expression 1: _?_ children and _?_ get off

    Expression 2: _?_ children

    Number sentence: _?_

Write a number sentence to compare the quantities in the situation.

2. Each of the 3 Drake children visit the jump house
    6 times. Violet visits the jump house 13 times.

3. There are 40 cups shared equally at 5 snack shops.
    There are 18 snack baskets.

4. There are 56 children riding the merry-go-round.
    There are 32 children riding the plane ride and
    21 children riding the Ferris wheel.

5. Edie had 22 carrot sticks on her salad. She took 5 of them
    off. Camille has 10 carrot sticks on her salad. Write a number
    sentence to compare how many carrot sticks each person has.

6. Kim has 10 plates. She put 4 pieces of lettuce on each plate.
    Marcy has 36 pieces of lettuce. Write a number sentence to
    compare the number of pieces of lettuce each person has.

TRY IT

Choose the answer.

7. George rode his bike 22 miles. He then rode 13 more miles. Helen rode 15 miles. Which number sentence compares the number of miles each person rode?

   A. $22 + 13 < 15$ B. $22 - 13 > 15$

   C. $22 + 13 > 15$ D. $22 - 13 < 15$

8. Paige took 35 pictures on her digital camera. She deleted 17 of them. Hannah took 45 pictures on her digital camera. Which number sentence compares how many pictures each person has on her camera?

   A. $35 - 17 < 45$ B. $35 - 17 > 45$

   C. $35 + 17 < 45$ D. $35 + 17 > 45$

TRY IT

Missing Symbols

Make It True

When solving for a missing operation or comparison symbol, find the value of expressions first.

Example:
Write the comparison symbol ($<$, $>$, $=$) to make the number sentence true.

$$\begin{array}{c} 12 \\ 5 + 7 \leq 13 \end{array}$$

Example:
Write the operation symbol ($+$, $-$, $\times$, $\div$) to make the number sentence true.

$$\begin{array}{c} 17 \\ 7 + 10 = 20 \underline{} 3 \end{array}$$

Write the operation symbol ($+$, $-$, $\times$, $\div$) that makes the number sentence true.

1. $15 \,\square\, 3 = 18$

2. $30 = 10 \,\square\, 3$

3. $20 \,\square\, 4 = 16$

4. $8 = 16 \,\square\, 2$

5. $6 + 7 = 21 \,\square\, 8$

6. $5 \,\square\, 4 = 9 + 11$

7. $15 \,\square\, 5 = 8 - 5$

8. $3 \times 10 = 24 \,\square\, 6$

TRY IT

Write the comparison symbol ($<$, $>$, $=$) that makes the number sentence true.

9. $16 + 7 \,\square\, 24$

10. $9 \,\square\, 14 - 5$

11. $55 \,\square\, 5 \times 10$

12. $47 - 13 \,\square\, 30$

13. $0 + 5 \,\square\, 3 \times 10$

14. $12 \,\square\, 4 \times 3$

15. $7 - 7 \,\square\, 7 - 0$

16. $28 + 12 \,\square\, 38$

T R Y   I T

Missing Values (A)

True Statements

Worked Examples

You can create an expression to make a number sentence true.

PROBLEM 1 Create an expression to make the number sentence true.

$$8 + 7 = \Box + \Box$$

SOLUTION Find the value of the expression you know: $8 + 7 = 15$.
Look at the operation in the unknown expression (addition).
Find numbers that add up to 15.

$$8 \overset{15}{+} 7 = \boxed{10} + \boxed{5}$$

ANSWER The answer can be any numbers with a sum of 15, such as $15 + 0$, $14 + 1$, or $13 + 2$.

PROBLEM 2 Create an expression to make the number sentence true.

$$\Box - \Box < 9 - 2$$

SOLUTION Find the value of the expression you know: $9 - 2 = 7$.

$$\Box - \Box < 9 \overset{7}{-} 2$$

Look at the comparison symbol (less than) and find a number less than 7 (such as 6). Find two numbers whose difference is 6 or less than 6.

$$\Box \overset{6}{-} \Box < 9 - 2$$

ANSWER $\boxed{9} - \boxed{3} < 9 - 2$

The answer can be any numbers whose difference is less than 7 such as $7 - 1$, $10 - 9$, or $100 - 95$.

Create an expression to make the number sentence true. Some problems have several correct answers.

1. $5 + 7 = \square + \square$

2. $8 + 8 = \square + \square$

3. $\square + \square = 6 - 4$

4. $\square + \square = 6 - 6$

5. $\square - \square = 4$

6. $\square - \square = 8 - 4$

7. $\square - \square < 8 - 4$

8. $\square - \square > 8 - 4$

Use sticky notes labeled 0–9. Place a note in the box to make the number sentence true. Use each note once. When you've finished, remove the sticky notes and record your answers.

9. $5 - \boxed{?} = 4$

10. $\boxed{?} + \boxed{?} = 5$

11. $13 - \boxed{?} = 7$

12. $\boxed{?} + 4 = 4$

13. $\boxed{?} + \boxed{?} = 9$

14. $\boxed{?} = 19 - 10$

15. $15 = \boxed{?} + \boxed{?}$

LEARN

Use sticky notes labeled 0–9. Place a note in the box to make the number sentence true. Use each note once. When you've finished, remove the sticky notes and record your answers.

16. $\boxed{?} + \boxed{?} < 2$ 17. $\boxed{?} + \boxed{?} < 6$

18. $11 > \boxed{?} + 6$ 19. $12 = \boxed{?} + \boxed{?}$

20. $14 < \boxed{?} + 6$ 21. $\boxed{?} < \boxed{?}$

Complete the number sentence to make it true.
Some problems have several correct answers.

22. $17 = 9 + \underline{\ ?\ }$

23. $17 < 9 + \underline{\ ?\ }$

24. $17 > 9 + \underline{\ ?\ }$

25. $8 + 9 < \underline{\ ?\ }$

26. $8 + 9 > \underline{\ ?\ }$

27. $17 - 9 < \underline{\ ?\ }$

LEARN

Missing Values (A)

What's Missing?

Complete the number sentence to make it true.
Some problems have several correct answers.

1. $8 + \square = 13$

2. $15 - \square = 12$

3. $\square - 5 = 17$

4. $\square = 17 - 9$

5. $18 - \square = 9$

6. $\square = 19 - 4$

7. $13 > \square + 9$

8. $11 + 2 > \square$

9. $6 + 5 = \square + \square$

T R Y   I T

Missing Values (B)

Multiplication and Division

Worked Examples

You can use arrays or grids to help you find missing numbers in multiplication and division number sentences.

PROBLEM 1 Use the array or grid to help find the missing number to make each number sentence true.

MULTIPLICATION

$35 = 5 \times \square$

$35 = 7 \times \square$

SOLUTION

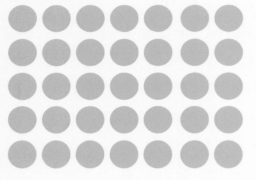

The array shows 5 rows of 7 or $5 \times 7 = 35$.

Turn the array sideways to show 7 rows of 5 or $7 \times 5 = 35$.

ANSWER

$35 = 5 \times 7$

$35 = 7 \times 5$

PROBLEM 2 Use the array or grid to help find the missing number to make each number sentence true.

DIVISION

$35 \div 5 = \square$

$35 \div 7 = \square$

SOLUTION

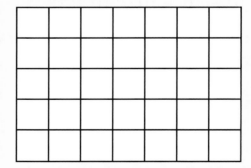

The grid shows 35 squares. Cut it into 5 rows of 7 squares to show that $35 \div 5 = 7$. Turn the grid sideways and cut it into 7 rows of 5 squares to show that $35 \div 7 = 5$.

ANSWER

$35 \div 5 = 7$

$35 \div 7 = 5$

LEARN

This array shows 3 rows of 5 circles. Use your blocks to make this array. Then use the array to help answer the questions.
Write the missing number to make the number sentence true.

1. $3 \times 5 = \square$

   $15 = \square \times 5$

   $5 + 5 + 5 = \square \times 5$

2. $5 \times 3 = \square$

   $9 + \square = 3 \times 5$

   $5 + 10 = \square$

Write the missing number to make the number sentence true.

3. $4 \times 10 = \square$

   $40 = \square \times 10$

   $10 + 10 + 10 + 10 = 10 \times \square$

   $60 - \square = 40$

   $4 \times 10 = \square + 20$

4. $2 \times 8 = \square$

   $8 + 8 = 8 \times \square$

   $8 \times \square = 16$

   $20 - \square = 2 \times 8$

   $8 + 8 = 10 + \square$

LEARN

Write the missing number. Use the grid to help.

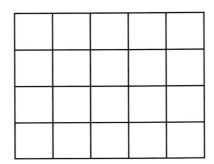

5. 3 groups of 5 is ☐.

   $3 \times 5 = $ ☐

   5 groups of ☐ is 15.

   $5 \times $ ☐ $= 15$

   $15 \div 5 = $ ☐

   $15 \div 3 = $ ☐

6. 4 groups of 5 is ☐.

   $20 \div 5 = $ ☐

   Think: ☐ $\times 5 = 20$

   5 groups of ☐ is 20.

   $20 \div 4 = $ ☐

   Think: $4 \times $ ☐ $= 20$

Write the missing number.

7. $10 \div $ ☐ $= 3 + 2$

8. $35 \div $ ☐ $= 5$

9. $10 = 20 \div $ ☐

10. $30 \div $ ☐ $= 10 - 7$

11. $8 \div $ ☐ $= 2 + 2$

12. $12 - 6 = 12 \div $ ☐

LEARN

Missing Values (B)

Missing Values in Number Sentences

Write the missing number.

1. $65 + \square = 92$

2. $87 - \square = 45$

3. $\square + 34 = 71$

4. $\square - 23 = 35$

5. $8 \times \square = 30 + 10$

6. $\square \times 3 = 10 - 4$

7. $30 \div \square = 3 \times 2$

8. $5 + 0 = 50 \div \square$

TRY IT

Missing Values (C)

Compare to Find Missing Values

Worked Examples

You can find a missing number to make a number sentence true.

PROBLEM Find a missing number to make the number sentence true.

$$2 \times 5 < 5 + ?$$

SOLUTION Find the value of the expression you know.

$$\overset{10}{2 \times 5} < 5 + ?$$

Look at the operation in the unknown expression (addition). Find a number that would make the expressions equal.

$$\overset{10}{2 \times 5} \overset{=}{<} 5 \overset{5+5}{+} ?$$

Find a number that would make the first expression less than the second expression.

$$\overset{10}{2 \times 5} < 5 + 6$$

ANSWER $2 \times 5 < 5 + 6$

The answer can be any number that is 6 or greater.

LEARN

Find a missing number to make the number sentence true.
Some problems have several correct answers.

1. $2 \times \underline{\ ?\ } = 10$

    $2 \times \underline{\ ?\ } < 10$

    $2 \times 5 > 8 + \underline{\ ?\ }$ **THINK** $10 > 8 + \underline{\ ?\ }$

2. $10 \div 2 = \underline{\ ?\ }$

    $10 \div 2 < \underline{\ ?\ }$

    $10 \div 2 > \underline{\ ?\ }$

    $10 \div 2 < 10 - \underline{\ ?\ }$ **THINK** $5 < 10 - \underline{\ ?\ }$

    $10 \div 2 > 0 + \underline{\ ?\ }$ **THINK** $5 > 0 + \underline{\ ?\ }$

3. $5 \times \underline{\ ?\ } > 20$ **THINK** $5 \times \underline{\ ?\ } = 20$

    $5 \times \underline{\ ?\ } < 25$

    $5 \times \underline{\ ?\ } > 4 + 4$ **THINK** $5 \times \underline{\ ?\ } > 8$

    $5 \times 2 < 8 + \underline{\ ?\ }$

    $8 \div 2 > \underline{\ ?\ }$

    $8 \div 2 < 4 + \underline{\ ?\ }$

4. $10 \times \underline{\ ?\ } < 30$

    $10 \times 2 > \underline{\ ?\ }$

    $10 \times 2 > 7 + \underline{\ ?\ }$

    $14 \div 2 < \underline{\ ?\ }$

    $14 \div 2 > 2 + \underline{\ ?\ }$

    $14 \div 2 < 10 - \underline{\ ?\ }$

L E A R N

Missing Values (C)

Simplify and Solve

Find a missing number to make the number sentence true.
The problems have several correct answers.

1. $35 > 20 + \underline{\ ?\ }$

2. $50 < 30 + \underline{\ ?\ }$

3. $\underline{\ ?\ } > 60 - 10$

4. $40 + \underline{\ ?\ } < 100$

5. $2 \times 5 < 7 + \underline{\ ?\ }$

6. $10 \div 2 > \underline{\ ?\ }$

7. $16 - 16 < 5 \times \underline{\ ?\ }$

8. $2 + \underline{\ ?\ } > 8 - 2$

TRY IT

Number Patterns

Find the Rule

Worked Examples

You can find a rule for a number pattern.

PROBLEM While counting the legs of horses in a field, Sarah saw this pattern: 4, 8, 12, 16.

| 4 | 8 | 12 | 16 |

What is the rule for this pattern?

SOLUTION Think about how the numbers change. Each number is 4 more than the previous number so the rule is: add 4.

ANSWER add 4

Identify the rule for the number pattern.

1. | 50 | 45 | 40 | 35 | 30 | 25 |

2. | 20 | 30 | 40 | 50 | 60 |

3. | 20 | 18 | 16 | 14 | 12 |

Fill in the missing numbers in the pattern and give the rule.

4. | 44 | ? | 54 | 59 | ? | ? |

L E A R N

Read the story problem and follow the directions.

5. Look at the nests and eggs chart. If you know how many nests there are, what is the rule to know how many eggs there are?

Eggs in a Nest	
Number of nests	**Number of eggs**
1	2
2	4
3	6
4	8
5	10

6. This chart shows how many birdhouses were sold and how much money was collected. If you know how many birdhouses were sold, what is the rule to know how much money was collected?

Birdhouses Sold	
Number of birdhouses	**Dollars collected**
1	$10
2	$20
3	$30
4	$40
5	$50

7. One ostrich egg weighs about 3 pounds. What rule can you use to find the weight of 10 ostrich eggs?

L E A R N

Number Patterns

Describe and Extend

Read the problem and follow the directions.

1. What number comes next in this pattern?
   23, 26, 29, 32, 35, 38, __?__

2. What number comes next in this pattern?
   13, 25, 37, 49, __?__

3. May counted down the number of days
   left in her vacation. She counted "21, 14, 7."
   Which rule describes the pattern?

Choose the answer.

4. Trish was watching people cross a bridge. She counted the
   number of feet she saw and said "2, 4, 6, 8, 10."
   Which rule describes this pattern?

   A. add 2   B. add 4

   C. add 10   D. add 12

5. Which pattern follows the rule "subtract 3"?

   A. 12, 9, 6, 1   B. 99, 66, 33, 11

   C. 55, 52, 49, 46   D. 3, 6, 9, 12

6. Which **two** rules describe this pattern?
   10, 15, 20, 25, 30

   A. add 5   B. add 10

   C. count by 5s   D. count by 10s

T R Y   I T

7. Which **two** rules describe this pattern?
6, 12, 18, 24, 30

A. add 6

B. add 10

C. count by 6s

D. count by 10s

8. Bala was practicing for a cross-country running competition. At the end of 1 week he had run 5 miles, at the end of 2 weeks he had run 10 miles, and at the end of 3 weeks he had run 15 miles. He made this chart to keep track. Which rule describes the pattern?

Running Distances	
Weeks	Total miles
1	5
2	10
3	15
4	20

A. add 10

B. add 7

C. multiply by 5

D. multiply by 10

Story Problems and Patterns (A)

Story Problems

Worked Examples

You can use patterns and an input-output table to solve story problems.

PROBLEM If each student needs 5 crayons, how many crayons are needed for the students shown in this table?

Input	Output
Number of students	**Number of crayons**
1	5
2	10
3	15
4	?
5	?
10	?
100	?

10 groups of 5 or
$10 \times 5 = 50$ crayons

100 groups of 5 crayons or
$100 \times 5 = 500$ crayons

ANSWER

Input	Output
Number of students	**Number of crayons**
1	5
2	10
3	15
4	20
5	25
10	50
100	500

SOLUTION Look at the table to find a pattern. Since each student gets 5 crayons, look at the number of students and count that many 5s. When the number of students jumps from 5 to 10, think of multiplication.

L E A R N

Complete the table using the rule.

1. Add 7. Subtract 1.

Input	Output
10	16
13	19
20	?
37	?
39	?

2. Multiply by 2.

Input	Output
5	10
8	16
10	?
12	?
16	?

Identify the pattern in the problem. Create a table to extend the pattern, and solve the problem.

3. One comic book costs $3. How much will 5 comic books cost? Create a table and fill in the missing values.

Choose the answer.

4. The table shows the number of bones needed for different numbers of dogs. If each dog gets the same number of bones, how many bones are needed for 4 dogs?

Number of dogs	Number of bones
1	2
2	4
3	6
4	?

A. 4   B. 6

C. 8   D. 10

LEARN

Story Problems and Patterns (A)

Tables and Patterns

Read the problem and solve.

1. Complete the input-output table by using the rule "add 5, subtract 2."

Input	Output
32	35
34	37
36	?
38	?
40	?

2. Complete the input-output table by using the rule "subtract 5, add 3."

Input	Output
5	3
10	8
15	?
20	?
25	?

3. LaBella is making a sign showing the cost to ski at Big Ski Hill. She wants to charge $12 per hour.

Big Ski Hill Prices	
Hours	Total cost
1	$12
2	$24
3	?
4	?

4. Frank is making a sign for his ice rink showing the cost to skate. He wants to charge $8 an hour.

Ice Skating Prices	
Hours	Total cost
1	$8
2	$16
3	?
4	?

T R Y   I T

Identify the pattern. Create a table to extend the pattern and solve.

5. It takes Anne 10 minutes to walk once around her block. She knows it will take 20 minutes to walk around the block 2 times and 30 minutes to walk around the block 3 times. How many minutes will it take Anne to walk around the block 5 times?

TRY IT

Story Problems and Patterns (B)

Beach Math

Worked Examples

You can use patterns and an input-output table to solve story problems.

PROBLEM How many wheels do you need for 10 skateboards?

SOLUTION Make an input-output table labeled as shown below. Fill in the number of wheels on different numbers of skateboards by adding 4 more wheels for each skateboard.

Input	Output
Number of skateboards	Number of wheels
1	4
2	8
3	12
4	16
5	20
6	24
7	28
8	32
9	36
10	40

Notice that you can count by 4s to fill in the numbers or you can think of multiplication.

10 skateboards have 10 groups of 4 wheels or $10 \times 4 = 40$ wheels.

ANSWER 40 wheels

Read the problem and solve.

1. Ice-cream cones are sold at the Beach Snack Shack. There are 3 scoops of ice cream on each cone. How many scoops of ice cream are needed for 7 ice-cream cones?

Number of ice-cream cones	Scoops of ice cream
1	3
2	6
3	9
4	12
5	15
6	18
7	?

2. Carmen collected 6 shells each day for 7 days. How many shells did Carmen have after 7 days?

Day	Number of shells
1	6
2	12
3	18
4	24
5	30
6	36
7	?

3. The Kayak Club rents kayaks for $10 an hour. How much would it cost to rent a kayak for 3 hours?

Hours	Total cost
1	$10
2	$20
3	?

4. Five people fit in 1 inner tube. How many people fit in 5 inner tubes?

Number of inner tubes	Number of people
1	5
2	10
3	15
4	?
5	?

Choose the answer.

5. Marc wants to buy beach balls for his friends. He knows that 1 beach ball costs $2, 2 beach balls cost $4, and 3 beach balls cost $6. How much will 4 beach balls cost?

   A. $7

   B. $8

   C. $9

   D. $10

6. A ride on the Ferris wheel costs $5 per person. How much would it cost for 6 people to ride the Ferris wheel?

   A. $5

   B. $10

   C. $25

   D. $30

LEARN

Story Problems and Patterns (B)

Make a Chart

Complete the table using the rule.

1. Add 5.

Input	Output
25	30
27	32
29	?
31	?
33	?

2. Multiply by 2. Add 3.

Input	Output
2	7
4	11
6	?
8	?
10	?

Make a table to solve the problem.

3. Each player gets 4 rings to toss at the ring toss game. How many rings are needed for 4 games?

4. Sam uses 6 lemons to make 1 glass of lemonade. How many lemons does Sam need to make 6 glasses of lemonade?

TRY IT

Model and Explain Multiplication
Model Multiplication

Use the picture of circle blocks to answer Problems 1–5.

1. How many groups are there?

2. How many objects are in each group?

3. What multiplication sentence is shown?

4. What addition sentence can you use to find the total?

5. How can you use a number line to find the total?

Use the picture of base-10 blocks to answer Problems 6 and 7.

6. How can you show 4×12 with addition?

7. What is the product or total?

Use the circle blocks to explain how to solve, and give the answer.

8. $4 \times 9 = \square$

Draw a sketch to show the answer, and give the answer.

9. $6 \times 2 = \square$

TRY IT

Use the pictures of frogs to answer the question.

10. Adrianna wants to know the total number of frogs in the ponds. Write one number sentence using addition and one number sentence using multiplication that she could use to solve the problem.

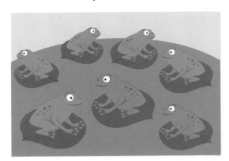 

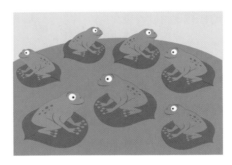

Choose the answer.

11. Hannah wants to know the total number of nuts in the bowls. Which **two** number sentences could she use?

   A. $4 + 4 + 4 + 4 + 4 + 4 = \square$

   B. $6 \times 6 = \square$

   C. $6 \times 4 = \square$

   D. $6 + 6 + 6 + 6 + 6 + 6 = \square$

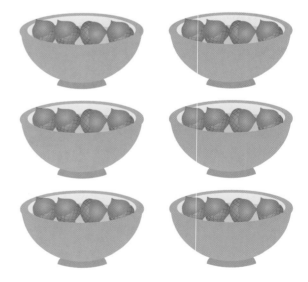

TRY IT

12. Which is another way to write $8 \times 2 = \square$?

A. $2 + 2 = \square$

B. $2 + 2 + 2 + 2 + 2 + 2 + 2 + 2 = \square$

C. $8 + 8 + 8 + 8 = \square$

D. $8 + 8 + 8 + 8 + 8 + 8 + 8 + 8 = \square$

13. Which shows $5 \times 6 = \square$?

A.

B.

C.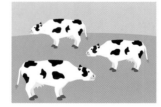

D.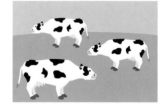

14. There are 7 fields. In each field there are 3 cows. What is the total number of cows in the fields?

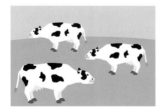  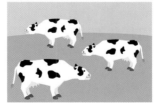

$$7 \times 3 = \square$$

A. 3   B. 7   C. 21   D. 28

TRY IT

Area Models for Multiplication (A)

Area Models

Use color tiles to show the multiplication expression.
Then find the product.

1. 6×3

2. 5×4

Multiply.

3. $2 \times 9 = \square$

4. $3 \times 9 = \square$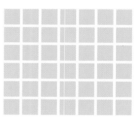

5. $4 \times 8 = \square$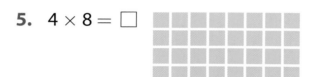

6. $6 \times 7 = \square$

Use grid paper to show how to solve the problem.

7. $6 \times 8 = \square$

8. $7 \times 5 = \square$

9. $8 \times 3 = \square$

TRY IT

Choose the answer.

10. Which shows $4 \times 5 = \square$?

A.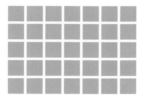

B.

C.

D.

11. $5 \times 7 = \square$
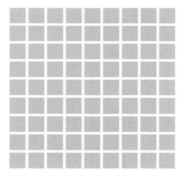

A. 7   B. 12   C. 30   D. 35

12. $9 \times 9 = \square$

A. 9   B. 18   C. 81   D. 99

T R Y   I T

Area Models for Multiplication (B)

Solve with Area Models

Answer the question.

1. Which model shows $17 \times 4 = \square$? Choose the answer.

A.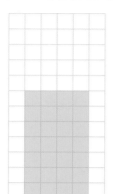

B.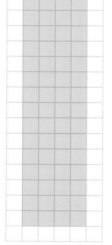

C.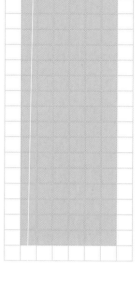

2. What is the product of $17 \times 4 = \square$?

3. Show 3×15 with an area model on grid paper.

4. Show how to use repeated addition to find 3×15.

5. How can you use the area model to find the product of 3×15?

TRY IT

Multiply.

6. $10 \times 4 = \square$

7. $13 \times 4 = \square$

Choose the answer.

8. Which shows $14 \times 2 = \square$?

A.

B.

C.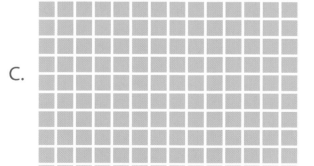

D. ▪▪▪▪▪▪▪▪▪▪▪▪▪▪▪▪▪▪▪▪▪▪▪▪▪▪

TRY IT

9. Which shows $5 \times 10 = \square$?

A.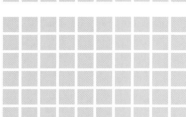

B.

C.

D.

10. $12 \times 3 = \square$

    A. 12

    B. 15

    C. 24

    D. 36

Understand Multiplication

Multiplication Results

Tell whether the product is zero, equal to one factor, or greater than both factors.

1. 5×6

2. 1×4

3. 3×0

4. 9×3

5. 0×5

6. 8×1

Answer the question.

7. Jared multiplies a number by 2. Will the product be even or odd? How do you know?

8. Look at this set of numbers: 10, 25, 35, 40, 50.
   Are these numbers multiples of 5? How do you know?

Choose the statement that is true.

9. Gina is going to multiply 5×6.

    A. It's impossible to know if the answer will be greater than 6.

    B. The answer is greater than 6.

    C. It's impossible to know if the answer will be less than 6.

    D. The answer is less than 6.

T R Y I T

10. Ralph is going to multiply two numbers greater than 1.

   A. The answer will sometimes be less than either number.

   B. The answer will always be less than either number.

   C. The answer will sometimes be greater than either number.

   D. The answer will always be greater than either number.

11. Rachel is going to use a number line to multiply 2×7.

   A. The answer will always be to the right of 7.

   B. The answer will sometimes be to the left of 7.

   C. The answer will always be to the left of 7.

   D. The answer will sometimes be to the right of 7.

12. Janice is going to multiply a whole number greater than zero by 10.

   A. The last digit in the product will be zero.

   B. The last digit in the product will always be 2.

   C. The last digit in the product will either be zero or 5.

   D. The product will always be an even number ending in 0, 2, 4, 6, or 8.

TRY IT

Commutative Property of Multiplication

Apply the Commutative Property

Use the commutative property of multiplication
to find the product.

1. $9 \times 5 = 45$
   $5 \times 9 = \underline{?}$

2. $7 \times 4 = 28$
   $4 \times 7 = \underline{?}$

3. $6 \times 8 = 48$
   $8 \times 6 = \underline{?}$

4. $3 \times 5 = 15$
   $5 \times 3 = \underline{?}$

Find the missing number.

5. $7 \times 3 = 3 \times \square$

6. $6 \times 4 = 4 \times \square$

7. $\square \times 2 = 2 \times 9$

8. $5 \times \square = 10 \times 5$

Change the order to make the numbers easier
to multiply. Then solve.

9. $2 \times 8 \times 5 = \square \times \square \times \square = \square$

10. $7 \times 6 \times 0 = \square \times \square \times \square = \square$

Answer the question.

11. Theresa knows that $8 \times 3 = 24$.
    Explain how she can quickly give the answer to 3×8
    by using the commutative property.

Choose the answer.

12. If $6 \times 3 = 18$, which sentence is true?

    A. The answer to 3×6 will be greater than 18.

    B. The answer to 3×6 will be equal to 18.

    C. The answer to 3×6 will be less than 18.

TRY IT

Multiplication Facts (A)

Practice Multiplication

Multiply.

1. $2 \times 3 = \underline{\ ?\ }$

2. $8 \times 4 = \underline{\ ?\ }$

3. $\begin{array}{r} 4 \\ \times\ 4 \\ \hline \end{array}$

4. $\begin{array}{r} 3 \\ \times\ 5 \\ \hline \end{array}$

5. $\begin{array}{r} 3 \\ \times\ 0 \\ \hline \end{array}$

6. $\begin{array}{r} 4 \\ \times\ 2 \\ \hline \end{array}$

7. $8 \times 3 = \underline{\ ?\ }$

8. $4 \times 6 = \underline{\ ?\ }$

9. $3 \times 4 = \underline{\ ?\ }$

10. $4 \times 10 = \underline{\ ?\ }$

11. $3 \times 1 = \underline{\ ?\ }$

12. $3 \times 10 = \underline{\ ?\ }$

13. $\begin{array}{r} 4 \\ \times\ 3 \\ \hline \end{array}$

14. $\begin{array}{r} 7 \\ \times\ 3 \\ \hline \end{array}$

15. $\begin{array}{r} 4 \\ \times\ 5 \\ \hline \end{array}$

16. $\begin{array}{r} 4 \\ \times\ 9 \\ \hline \end{array}$

17. $7 \times 4 = \underline{\ ?\ }$

18. $6 \times 3 = \underline{\ ?\ }$

19. $4 \times 1 = \underline{\ ?\ }$

20. $3 \times 3 = \underline{\ ?\ }$

21. $1 \times 4 = \underline{\ ?\ }$

22. $6 \times 4 = \underline{\ ?\ }$

23. $4 \times 8 = \underline{\ ?\ }$

24. $9 \times 4 = \underline{\ ?\ }$

25. $\begin{array}{r} 10 \\ \times\ 4 \\ \hline \end{array}$

26. $\begin{array}{r} 0 \\ \times\ 10 \\ \hline \end{array}$

TRY IT

Multiplication Facts (B)

Facts for 6 and 7

Multiply.

1. $\begin{array}{r} 6 \\ \times\ 3 \\ \hline \end{array}$

2. $\begin{array}{r} 7 \\ \times\ 9 \\ \hline \end{array}$

3. $\begin{array}{r} 7 \\ \times\ 7 \\ \hline \end{array}$

4. $\begin{array}{r} 6 \\ \times\ 8 \\ \hline \end{array}$

5. $\begin{array}{r} 6 \\ \times\ 5 \\ \hline \end{array}$

6. $\begin{array}{r} 6 \\ \times\ 1 \\ \hline \end{array}$

7. $\begin{array}{r} 7 \\ \times\ 4 \\ \hline \end{array}$

8. $\begin{array}{r} 7 \\ \times\ 3 \\ \hline \end{array}$

9. $\begin{array}{r} 9 \\ \times\ 7 \\ \hline \end{array}$

10. $\begin{array}{r} 2 \\ \times\ 6 \\ \hline \end{array}$

11. $\begin{array}{r} 6 \\ \times\ 7 \\ \hline \end{array}$

12. $\begin{array}{r} 4 \\ \times\ 5 \\ \hline \end{array}$

13. $7 \times 6 = \underline{\ ?\ }$

14. $4 \times 5 = \underline{\ ?\ }$

15. $8 \times 6 = \underline{\ ?\ }$

16. $3 \times 7 = \underline{\ ?\ }$

17. $6 \times 10 = \underline{\ ?\ }$

18. $0 \times 3 = \underline{\ ?\ }$

19. $7 \times 1 = \underline{\ ?\ }$

20. $9 \times 7 = \underline{\ ?\ }$

21. $7 \times 2 = \underline{\ ?\ }$

22. $7 \times 6 = \underline{\ ?\ }$

23. $2 \times 7 = \underline{\ ?\ }$

24. $3 \times 6 = \underline{\ ?\ }$

25. $5 \times 7 = \underline{\ ?\ }$

26. $7 \times 6 = \underline{\ ?\ }$

27. $9 \times 6 = \underline{\ ?\ }$

28. $10 \times 7 = \underline{\ ?\ }$

TRY IT

Multiplication Facts (C)

Multiplication Minutes

Multiply.

1. $\begin{array}{r} 8 \\ \times\ 8 \\ \hline \end{array}$	**2.** $\begin{array}{r} 9 \\ \times\ 8 \\ \hline \end{array}$	**3.** $\begin{array}{r} 9 \\ \times\ 9 \\ \hline \end{array}$	**4.** $\begin{array}{r} 6 \\ \times\ 5 \\ \hline \end{array}$	**5.** $\begin{array}{r} 9 \\ \times\ 1 \\ \hline \end{array}$
6. $\begin{array}{r} 9 \\ \times\ 4 \\ \hline \end{array}$	**7.** $\begin{array}{r} 2 \\ \times\ 7 \\ \hline \end{array}$	**8.** $\begin{array}{r} 9 \\ \times\ 3 \\ \hline \end{array}$	**9.** $\begin{array}{r} 7 \\ \times\ 9 \\ \hline \end{array}$	**10.** $\begin{array}{r} 8 \\ \times\ 2 \\ \hline \end{array}$

11. $8 \times 10 = \underline{\ ?\ }$

12. $5 \times 8 = \underline{\ ?\ }$

13. $1 \times 8 = \underline{\ ?\ }$

14. $3 \times 4 = \underline{\ ?\ }$

15. $9 \times 10 = \underline{\ ?\ }$

16. $8 \times 3 = \underline{\ ?\ }$

17. $9 \times 5 = \underline{\ ?\ }$

18. $8 \times 9 = \underline{\ ?\ }$

19. $9 \times 2 = \underline{\ ?\ }$

20. $9 \times 6 = \underline{\ ?\ }$

21. $1 \times 9 = \underline{\ ?\ }$

22. $3 \times 8 = \underline{\ ?\ }$

23. $4 \times 9 = \underline{\ ?\ }$

24. $5 \times 8 = \underline{\ ?\ }$

25. $6 \times 9 = \underline{\ ?\ }$

26. $8 \times 8 = \underline{\ ?\ }$

TRY IT

Associative Property

Group and Multiply

Group the factors another way.

1. $(7 \times 8) \times 9$

2. $3 \times (4 \times 6)$

Use parentheses to show which factors you will multiply first. Then find the value of the expression.

3. $4 \times 5 \times 2$

4. $2 \times 3 \times 8$

5. $5 \times 5 \times 3$

Solve.

6. Gordon knows that $7 \times (3 \times 4) = 84$. What does $(7 \times 3) \times 4$ equal?

7. What number replaces the box to make this a true sentence? $(8 \times 12) \times 3 = 8 \times (\Box \times 3)$

Choose the answer.

8. Terry knows that $(3 \times 5) \times 2 = 30$. What is the answer to $3 \times (5 \times 2) = \underline{?}$

   A. 6   B. 10   C. 15   D. 30

9. If $4 \times (9 \times 8) = 288$, then what is $(4 \times 9) \times 8$?

   A. 36   B. 44   C. 72   D. 288

10. If $(11 \times 5) \times 12 = 660$, which sentence is true?

    A. The answer to $11 \times (5 \times 12)$ will be less than 660.

    B. The answer to $11 \times (5 \times 12)$ will be equal to 660.

    C. The answer to $11 \times (5 \times 12)$ will be greater than 660.

TRY IT

Multiplication Story Problems

Model Multiplication Story Problems

Worked Examples

You can use objects or sketches to solve multiplication story problems.

PROBLEM 1 Farmer Jane plants 3 rows of seeds. She plants 10 seeds in each row. How many seeds does Farmer Jane plant?

SOLUTION

1 Model 3 rows with 10 circles in each row.

⬤⬤⬤⬤⬤⬤⬤⬤⬤⬤
⬤⬤⬤⬤⬤⬤⬤⬤⬤⬤
⬤⬤⬤⬤⬤⬤⬤⬤⬤⬤

2 Write the multiplication number sentence. $3 \times 10 = ?$

$$3 \qquad \times \qquad 10 \qquad = \qquad ?$$

| number of rows | number of seeds in each row | total number of seeds |

ANSWER $3 \times 10 = 30$; Farmer Jane uses 30 seeds.

PROBLEM 2 Ted has 6 vases. He puts 5 flowers in each vase. How many flowers does Ted use?

SOLUTION

1 Sketch 6 vases with 5 flowers in each vase.

LEARN

2 Write the multiplication number sentence. $5 \times 6 = ?$

6	×	5	=	?
number of vases		number of flowers in each vase		total number of flowers

ANSWER $6 \times 5 = 30$; Ted uses 30 flowers.

PROBLEM 3 Simone made 4 posters. She put 34 stickers on each poster. How many stickers did Simone use in all?

SOLUTION

1 Use base-10 blocks to make 4 groups of 34.
Each group will have 3 tens rods and 4 ones cubes.

2 Group all the tens rods together and all the ones cubes together. Skip count by 10s and then count on by ones to find the total, 136.

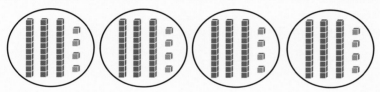

3 Write the multiplication number sentence. $4 \times 34 = ?$

4	×	34	=	?
posters		stickers on each poster		total number of stickers

ANSWER $4 \times 34 = 136$; Simone used 136 stickers in all.

LEARN

Use circle blocks to model the problem.
Write the multiplication number sentence and solve.

1. Farmer Ted has 8 containers. He puts 2 tomato plants in each container. How many tomato plants does he use?

2. There are 7 baskets of peppers. There are 5 peppers in each basket. How many peppers are there altogether?

Make a sketch to model the problem.
Write the multiplication number sentence and solve.

3. Jane buys 2 bags of onions. There are 10 small onions in each bag. How many onions are there in all?

4. There are 9 shelves. There are 3 pumpkins on each shelf. How many pumpkins are on the shelves altogether?

Use base-10 blocks to model the problem.
Write the multiplication number sentence and solve.

5. Andre has 4 packs of seeds. Each pack has 32 seeds. How many seeds does Andre have?

LEARN

Multiplication Story Problems

Model and Solve Problems

Use the model to solve.

1. Ryan has 4 boxes of model cars. There are 7 cars in each box. How many model cars does Ryan have in all?

$4 \times 7 = \underline{?}$

2. Jessie placed her seashells in 3 piles. She put 24 shells in each pile. How many seashells does Jessie have altogether?

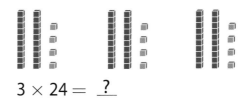

$3 \times 24 = \underline{?}$

3. Dawn has 8 bags of bagels. Each bag has 4 bagels in it. How many bagels does Dawn have? Choose the answer.

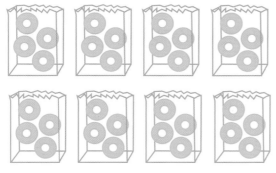

A. 8

B. 16

C. 12

D. 32

4. A carton of eggs has 2 rows. There are 6 eggs in each row. How many eggs are in the carton? Choose the answer.

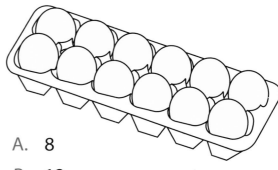

A. 8

B. 12

C. 16

D. 24

TRY IT

Use circles or sketches to model and solve.

5. Cole has a bookshelf with 5 shelves. He places 4 books on each shelf. How many books are on the bookshelf?
$5 \times 4 = \underline{\ ?\ }$

6. There are 7 picnic benches at the park. There are 6 children on each bench. How many children are sitting on the benches in all?
$7 \times 6 = \underline{\ ?\ }$

Use circles or sketches to model. Write the multiplication number sentence and solve.

7. Theo has 5 bags of peaches. There are 5 peaches in each bag. How many peaches does Theo have altogether?

8. There are 8 baskets of strawberries. There are 10 strawberries in each basket. How many strawberries are there in all?

Use circles to model and solve.

9. Alyssa has 3 boxes of crayons. Each box has 8 crayons. How many crayons does Alyssa have?

10. Tom has 3 fields on his farm. Each field has 7 cows. How many cows are on Tom's farm?

11. Rachel has 4 boxes of buttons. Each box has 7 buttons. How many buttons does Rachel have?

Draw a sketch to model and solve.

12. Daniel is putting some muffins into a container. He makes 5 rows of muffins. He puts 2 muffins in each row. How many muffins does Daniel have?

13. Jeanie bought some stamps. There were 4 rows of stamps. Each row had 5 stamps. How many stamps did Jeanie buy?

14. Sarah had a tray of juice boxes. She put 3 rows of juice boxes on the tray. Each row had 5 juice boxes. How many juice boxes did Sarah have?

TRY IT

Memory Jogger

TWO WAYS TO MULTIPLY

Here are two ways to multiply a single-digit number by a multidigit number.

Find Partial Products

$$\begin{array}{r} 248 \\ \times \quad 6 \\ \hline \end{array}$$

$$\begin{array}{r} 200 \ + \ 40 \ + \ 8 \\ \times \quad 6 \\ \hline 1{,}200 \ + \ 240 \ + \ 48 \end{array}$$

$$\mathbf{1{,}488}$$

Write 248 in expanded form by writing the number as hundreds, tens, and ones.

Multiply the parts: 6×200; then 6×40; then 6×8.

Add the parts. (Try to add them in your head.) $1{,}200 + 240 + 40 + 8$

Use the Algorithm

Multiply the ones.	Multiply the tens.	Multiply the hundreds.
$$\begin{array}{r} {}^{4} \\ 248 \\ \times \quad 6 \\ \hline 8 \end{array}$$	$$\begin{array}{r} {}^{2\,4} \\ 248 \\ \times \quad 6 \\ \hline 88 \end{array}$$	$$\begin{array}{r} {}^{2\,4} \\ 248 \\ \times \quad 6 \\ \hline 1{,}488 \end{array}$$
($6 \times 8 = 48$ or 4 tens and 8 ones)	(6×4 tens $= 24$ tens; then add the 4 tens that were regrouped to get 28 tens)	(6×2 hundreds $= 12$ hundreds; then add the 2 hundreds that were regrouped to get 14 hundreds)

TRY IT

Multiply. Use partial products or the standard algorithm.

1. 32
     × 3

2. 152
     ×   4

3. 870
     ×   5

4. 64
     × 8

5. 2,983
     ×   6

6. 4,098
     ×   3

7. 923
     ×   4

Choose the answer.

8. 67
     × 3

A. 201
B. 181
C. 70
D. 21

9. 55
     × 2

A. 1,110
B. 110
C. 101
D. 57

10. 237
      ×   7

A. 1,419
B. 1,459
C. 1,619
D. 1,659

11. 145
      ×   5

A. 505
B. 525
C. 705
D. 725

12. 3,021
      ×   4

A. 16,484
B. 16,084
C. 12,484
D. 12,084

T R Y   I T

Multiply Equal Groups (A)

Multiplication Story Problems

You can multiply to solve story problems that involve equal groups.

PROBLEM An ant has 6 legs. How many legs would there be in a colony of 1,500 ants?

SOLUTION Multiply to solve the problem. Use the method that is easiest for you.

1 Turn the problem into a sentence. $6 \times 1,500 = ?$

2 Solve using partial products.

$$
\begin{array}{r}
1,500 \\
\times \quad 6 \\
\hline
\end{array}
\qquad \longrightarrow \qquad
\begin{array}{r}
1,000 \;+\; 500 \\
\times \quad 6 \qquad\quad 6 \\
\hline
6,000 \;+\; 3,000 \\
\mathbf{9,000}
\end{array}
$$

or

Solve using the algorithm.
Multiply the ones.
$$
\begin{array}{r}
1,500 \\
\times \quad 6 \\
\hline
0
\end{array}
$$

Multiply the tens.
$$
\begin{array}{r}
1,500 \\
\times \quad 6 \\
\hline
00
\end{array}
$$

Multiply the hundreds.
$$
\begin{array}{r}
^{3} \\
1,500 \\
\times \quad 6 \\
\hline
000
\end{array}
$$

Multiply the thousands.
$$
\begin{array}{r}
^{3} \\
1,500 \\
\times \quad 6 \\
\hline
9,000
\end{array}
$$

ANSWER $6 \times 1,500 = 9,000$
There would be 9,000 legs.

L E A R N

Multiply to solve each problem.

1. A sheep has 4 feet.
   There are 200 sheep in the herd.
   How many feet are there altogether?

   _?_ feet

2. A chicken has 2 legs.
   There are 67 chickens in the coop.
   How many legs are there altogether?

   _?_ legs

3. An octopus has 8 arms.
   If there are 642 octopuses in the ocean, how many
   arms are there altogether?

   _?_ arms

4. A starfish has 5 arms.
   There are 830 starfish at the aquarium.
   How many arms are there altogether?

   _?_ arms

Multiply Equal Groups (A)

Multiply Groups and Objects

Solve.

1. Sally bought 4 apples for each person in her family. There are 3 people in Sally's family. How many apples did Sally buy?

2. Oliver has a box of avocados. There are 6 rows of avocados. Each row has 7 avocados. How many avocados are in the box?

3. A baker bought 3 large cartons of eggs. There were 18 eggs in each carton. How many eggs did the baker buy?

4. A store has 10 fish tanks. There are 5 fish in each tank. How many fish are in the fish tanks?

Choose the answer.

5. Shirley is putting new tile on the wall behind her sink. She is putting 5 rows of tiles on the wall. There will be 18 tiles in each row. How many tiles does Shirley need?

    A. 23   B. 40   C. 90   D. 108

6. Frida has 12 bowls. Each bowl has 4 apples. What is the total number of apples in the bowls?

    A. 16   B. 24   C. 48   D. 52

7. The cafeteria had a display of milk bottles. There were 6 rows of milk bottles. Each row had 12 milk bottles. How many milk bottles were in the display?

    A. 12   B. 18   C. 66   D. 72

TRY IT

Multiply Equal Groups (B)

Multiplication Computation

Worked Examples

You can multiply to solve story problems with equal groups.

PROBLEM There are 8 crayons in a mini box. How many crayons are in a crate of 347 mini boxes? $347 \times 8 = ?$

SOLUTION 1
Find partial products.

$$\begin{array}{r} 347 \\ \times\ \ 8 \\ \hline \end{array}$$

$$\begin{array}{r} 300\ +\ \ 40\ +\ \ 7 \\ \times\ \ 8 \\ \hline 2{,}400\ +\ 320\ +\ 56 \\ \hline 2{,}776 \end{array}$$

Try to add this in your head:
$2{,}400 + 320 + 50 + 6$

SOLUTION 2
Use the algorithm.

$$\begin{array}{r} {}^{3\,5}347 \\ \times\qquad 8 \\ \hline 2{,}776 \end{array}$$

ANSWER
$$\begin{array}{r} 347 \\ \times\ \ 8 \\ \hline 2{,}776 \end{array}$$
There are 2,776 crayons in a crate of 347 mini boxes.

Multiply.

1. At the museum, the tour guides did 7 tours a day. Each tour had 129 people. How many people took tours altogether?

   $? \times ? = ?$

2. The flower show had 6 showrooms of flowers. Each room had 1,027 flowers. How many flowers were there altogether?

   $? \times ? = ?$

LEARN

Multiply Equal Groups (B)

Multiply to Solve

Solve.

1. Janelle bought 6 large boxes of mangos. There were 14 mangos in each box. How many mangos did Janelle buy?

2. The camp counselor gave 3 plums to each camper. There were 125 campers. How many plums did the counselor give out?

3. Kelly knit 9 rows in her sweater. Each row had 203 stitches. How many stitches did Kelly knit?

4. A nut factory had 1,987 almonds in each crate. If there were 4 crates, how many almonds did the factory have?

Choose the answer.

5. Simone was paving a pathway in her yard. She had 9 rows of small paving stones. Each row had 102 stones. How many paving stones did she use?

   A. 102   B. 111

   C. 908   D. 918

6. The caterer has 106 plates. He wants to put 4 potatoes on each plate. How many potatoes does the caterer need?

   A. 424   B. 404

   C. 110   D. 64

7. Cindy drew some squares on her paper. She drew 15 rows of squares. Each row had 6 squares. How many squares did Cindy draw?

   A. 105   B. 90

   C. 75   D. 21

8. A grocery store had 5 crates of toothpaste. Each crate had 1,921 tubes of toothpaste. How many tubes of toothpaste did the grocery store have?

   A. 5,505   B. 5,605

   C. 9,505   D. 9,605

TRY IT

Multiplication with Equal Measures

Equal-Measures Story Problems

Worked Examples

You can multiply to solve story problems with equal measures.

PROBLEM Tara knitted a scarf that was 48 inches long. If she knits 6 scarves, how many inches will she have knitted?

SOLUTION Find the amount that gets added over and over. Find the number of times this amount gets added. Write the multiplication number sentence you can use to multiply these amounts. Solve using partial products or the algorithm.

Find partial products.

$$
\begin{array}{r}
48 \\
\times\ 6 \\
\end{array}
\qquad
\begin{array}{r}
40\ +\ 8 \\
\times\ \ \ \ 6 \\
\hline
240\ +\ 48 \\
288 \\
\end{array}
$$

Use the algorithm.

$$
\begin{array}{r}
\overset{4}{4}8 \\
\times\ 6 \\
\hline
8 \\
\end{array}
\qquad
\begin{array}{r}
\overset{4}{4}8 \\
\times\ 6 \\
\hline
288 \\
\end{array}
$$

ANSWER $6 \times 48 = 288$

Tara will have knitted 288 inches.

Solve.

1. A hot-air balloon travels 5 miles in one hour.

   How many miles will the balloon travel in 3 hours?

2. A go-cart takes 42 seconds to complete one lap.

   How many seconds will it take to complete 7 laps?

LEARN

3. There are 8 ounces in one cup.

   How many ounces are in 30 cups?

4. If you walk 4 laps every morning, how many laps will you have walked after 18 days?

5. Mr. Peterson spends $130 at the grocery store every week.

   How much money will he spend in 4 weeks?

6. If a boy grows 2 inches a year for 6 years, how many inches in all will he grow?

Multiplication with Equal Measures

Solve Equal–Measures Story Problems

Solve.

1. Eli bought 3 bunches of roses. If each bunch cost $9, how much did Eli spend on roses?

2. Freddie charged $88 for a car tune-up. He did a tune-up on 6 vehicles last month. How much did he earn doing tune-ups last month?

3. Megan buys 110 pounds of dog food a year for each dog. How much will Megan need to buy for 2 dogs?

4. There are 1,760 yards in 1 mile. How many yards are in 5 miles?

Choose the answer.

5. Monica ran 2 miles each day for 5 days. What is the total distance Monica ran?

   A. 7 miles   B. 10 miles

   C. 15 miles   D. 20 miles

6. Mia earns $250 every month. How much will Mia earn in 7 months?

   A. $1,400   B. $1,450

   C. $1,750   D. $1,850

7. The blue whale is as long as 6 elephants put together. If each elephant is 15 feet long, how long is a blue whale?

   A. 60 feet   B. 90 feet

   C. 95 feet   D. 100 feet

8. Melanie is renting a house. The rent costs $1,850 each month. How much will she have to pay for 4 months?

   A. $4,200   B. $4,400

   C. $7,200   D. $7,400

TRY IT

Write Multiplication Stories (A)

Types of Multiplication Story Problems

Worked Examples

There are different types of multiplication story problems, including
- **Area model** (squares in a rectangular grid)
- **Array** (rows of objects with the same number in each row)
- **Equal groups** (same number of objects in each pile)
- **Equal measures** (same measure many times)

PROBLEM Read the story problem, and tell which type it is.
- The farmer covered the hamster yard with grass squares. He covered the yard with 9 rows. There are 12 grass squares in each row. How many grass squares did the farmer use in all?

SOLUTION This problem describes squares of grass that are right next to each other with no space in between. The squares form a grid, so the area model is best model for the problem.

ANSWER area model

Tell what type of multiplication story problem best matches the problem, and why.

1. There are 365 hamsters on the hamster farm. Each hamster eats 3 hamster pellets for lunch. How many pellets will the hamsters eat altogether during one lunch?

2. If Hamie Hamster runs around the exercise wheel 40 times each day for one week, how many times did he go around the wheel altogether? (Hint: 1 week = 7 days)

3. Marta is making a scrapbook of hamster pictures. She can fit 3 square pictures side-by-side in each row, with the edges touching. There are 24 rows in all. How many pictures are there altogether?

4. The hamster cages are lined up in 5 rows with 28 cages in each row. How many cages are there in all?

5. Marta is entering 4 of her hamsters in a pet show. Each hamster will wear a bow made from a 7-inch ribbon. How much ribbon will Marta need to make the bows?

6. The pet store has a box of hamster food. The box has 3 rows of cans and each row has 6 cans. How many cans of hamster food are in the box?

LEARN

Model and Explain Division

Represent Division Problems

Use repeated subtraction to solve the problem.

1. $18 \div 6 = \underline{}$

2. $36 \div 9 = \underline{}$

Use circle blocks to solve the problem.

3. $35 \div 7 = \underline{}$

4. $\underline{} = 28 \div 7$

Draw a sketch to show how to solve the problem.

5. $\underline{} = 18 \div 3$

6. $20 \div 4 = \underline{}$

Use circle blocks to show how to use repeated subtraction to solve the problem.

7. Kristina has 18 grapes.
   She wants to give 2 grapes to each person.

   How many people can she give grapes to?

8. Mark has 40 tiles.
   He wants to put 4 tiles onto each tray.

   How many trays will Mark need?

Use a sketch to solve the problem.

9. Johnny has a bag of 12 cat treats.
   He gives 3 treats to each cat.

   How many cats are there?

TRY IT

Choose the answer.

10. Geoff wanted to solve this problem.

    $25 \div 5 = ?$

    Which operation should he use?

    A. addition

    B. multiplication

    C. subtraction

    D. division

11. Kent wanted to solve this problem.

    $? = 36 \div 6$

    Which operation should he use?

    A. subtraction

    B. addition

    C. division

    D. multiplication

12. Which sketch shows $15 \div 3 = ?$

    A.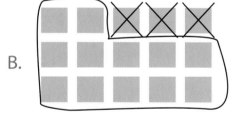

    B.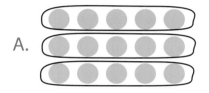

    C.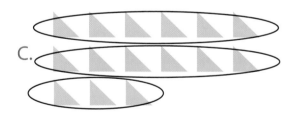

    D.

TRY IT

Applying Division Symbols and Rules

Division Symbols and Properties

THREE WAYS TO WRITE DIVISION PROBLEMS

Division problems can be written three ways.
No matter how you write a problem, you say it the same way.

Division Sentence	Say	Write
$12 \div 4 = 3$	12 divided by 4 equals 3	12 and say "divided by" as you write the standard division symbol
$\frac{12}{4} = 3$	12 divided by 4 equals 3	12 and say "divided by" as you write the fraction bar
$4\overline{)12}$ with 3 above	12 divided by 4 equals 3	12 and say "divided by" as you write the long-division symbol, $\overline{)}$

Answer the question.

1. Show three different ways to write 12 divided by 3.

2. Show three different ways to write 18 divided by 6.

Explain how to solve the problem.

3. $9 \div 0 = ?$

4. $? = 0 \div 7$

5. $4 \div 1 = ?$

6. $? = 8 \div 1$

Choose the answer.

7. $10 \div 0 = ?$

    A. 1

    B. 0

    C. 10

    D. There is no answer.

8. $10 \div 1 = ?$

    A. 10

    B. 0

    C. 1

    D. There is no answer.

9. $9 \div 1 = ?$

    A. 1

    B. 9

    C. 0

    D. There is no answer.

10. Which is another way to write $20 \div 4 = ?$

    A. $4 \div 20 = ?$

    B. $20 \overline{)\,4\,} = ?$

    C. $\frac{20}{4} = ?$

T R Y   I T

Division as Sharing

Explain Division

Draw a sketch to show how to solve the problem.
Give your answer.

1. Aisha wanted to put 15 muffins in a box. She could put 3 muffins in each row. How many rows would she need?

2. Destiny wanted to put 18 baseballs in 3 bags. If she put the same number of baseballs in each bag, how many baseballs would she put in each bag?

Use circle blocks to show how to solve the problem.
Give your answer.

3. Julianne has 42 marbles to share with 6 people. She wants to give each person the same number of marbles. How many marbles will each person get?

4. Frankie has 36 carrot sticks to share with 4 people. He wants to give each person the same number of carrot sticks. How many carrot sticks will each person get?

Choose the answer.

5. Beverly wanted to solve this problem. Thirty avocado trees were planted in 5 rows. There were the same number of trees in each row. How many trees were planted in each row?

Which shows a correct way to solve this problem?

A.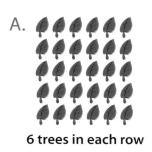
6 trees in each row

B.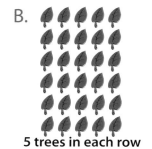
5 trees in each row

C.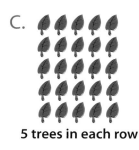
5 trees in each row

D.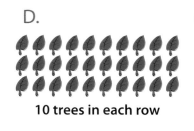
10 trees in each row

6. Maria wanted to solve this problem. The band director wants his band marching in 3 equal columns. If there are 24 members in the band, how many will be in each column?

Which shows a correct way to solve this problem?

A.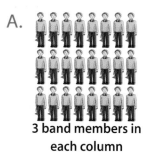
3 band members in each column

B.
4 band members in each column

C.
8 band members in each column

D.
6 band members in each column

TRY IT

Relating Multiplication and Division

Inverse Operations

Write the related fact to complete the fact family.

1. $5 \times 2 = 10$
$2 \times 5 = 10$
$10 \div 5 = 2$
$\underline{?} \div \underline{?} = \underline{?}$

2. $21 \div 3 = 7$
$21 \div 7 = 3$
$7 \times 3 = 21$
$\underline{?} \times \underline{?} = \underline{?}$

Choose the answer.

3. Carlos drew this sketch to solve $9 \times 3 = ?$

This sketch could also be used to solve which division problem?

A. $3 \div 9 = ?$

B. $9 \div 3 = ?$

C. $3 \div 27 = ?$

D. $27 \div 3 = ?$

4. Richard drew this sketch to solve $8 \times 4 = ?$

This sketch could also be used to solve which division problem?

A. $32 \div 4 = ?$

B. $8 \div 32 = ?$

C. $8 \div 4 = ?$

D. $4 \div 8 = ?$

5. Cathleen drew this sketch to solve $16 \div 2 = ?$

This sketch could also be used to solve which multiplication problem?

A. $8 \times 2 = ?$

B. $2 \times 16 = ?$

C. $16 \times 8 = ?$

D. $2 \times 8 \times 16 = ?$

6. Grace drew this sketch to solve $27 \div 3 = ?$

This sketch could also be used to solve which multiplication problem?

A. $3 \times 27 = ?$

B. $9 \times 27 = ?$

C. $3 \times 9 \times 27 = ?$

D. $9 \times 3 = ?$

TRY IT

7. Gunnar used these circles to solve $? = 32 \div 8$. These circles could also be used to solve which problem?

A. $8 + 32 = ?$

B. $32 - 8 = ?$

C. $4 \times 8 = ?$

D. $32 \times 8 = ?$

8. Pete used these circles to solve $? = 16 \div 2$. These circles could also be used to solve which problem?

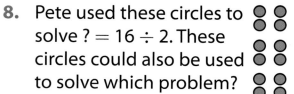

A. $? = 2 + 8$

B. $? = 2 - 8$

C. $? = 2 \times 16$

D. $? = 2 \times 8$

9. Charlotte and Jordan each wrote a number sentence to solve this problem.

Tanya bought 18 plums. She ate 2 plums every day. How many days will the plums last?

Charlotte wrote this number sentence: $18 \div 2 = ?$

Jordan's number sentence was different but was also correct.

Which number sentence could Jordan have written?

A. $? \times 2 = 18$

B. $2 \times 18 = ?$

C. $? = 18 \times 2$

D. $? = 18 - 2$

10. Diana and Alex each wrote a number sentence to solve this problem.

John can run one lap in 3 minutes. If he keeps the same pace, how long will it take him to run 5 laps?

Diana wrote this number sentence: $5 \times 3 = ?$

Alex's number sentence was different but was also correct.

Which number sentence could Alex have written?

A. $? \div 3 = 5$

B. $? - 3 = 5$

C. $? + 3 = 5$

D. $3 \div 5 = ?$

TRY IT

Use Inverse Relationships

Check with Multiplication

Worked Examples

You can use what you know about the inverse relationships between multiplication and division to find the missing facts in a multiplication fact family.

PROBLEM Complete the fact family.

$7 \times 9 = 63$　　　$\underline{\ ?\ } \div \underline{\ ?\ } = \underline{\ ?\ }$

$\underline{\ ?\ } \times \underline{\ ?\ } = \underline{\ ?\ }$　　　$\underline{\ ?\ } \div \underline{\ ?\ } = \underline{\ ?\ }$

SOLUTION

1 Look at the multiplication fact that's given ($7 \times 9 = 63$), and write the related fact ($9 \times 7 = 63$).

2 Write the inverse to both facts.

ANSWER　　　$7 \times 9 = 63$　　　$63 \div 9 = 7$

　　　　　　　　$9 \times 7 = 63$　　　$63 \div 7 = 9$

Complete the fact family.

1. $8 \times 7 = 56$　　　$\underline{\ ?\ } \div \underline{\ ?\ } = \underline{\ ?\ }$

　　$\underline{\ ?\ } \times \underline{\ ?\ } = \underline{\ ?\ }$　　　$\underline{\ ?\ } \div \underline{\ ?\ } = \underline{\ ?\ }$

2. $5 \times 9 = 45$　　　$\underline{\ ?\ } \div \underline{\ ?\ } = \underline{\ ?\ }$

　　$\underline{\ ?\ } \times \underline{\ ?\ } = \underline{\ ?\ }$　　　$\underline{\ ?\ } \div \underline{\ ?\ } = \underline{\ ?\ }$

3. $20 \div 4 = 5$　　　$\underline{\ ?\ } \times \underline{\ ?\ } = \underline{\ ?\ }$

　　$\underline{\ ?\ } \div \underline{\ ?\ } = \underline{\ ?\ }$　　　$\underline{\ ?\ } \times \underline{\ ?\ } = \underline{\ ?\ }$

LEARN

You can use the inverse relationship between multiplication and division to check your work in a division problem.

PROBLEM Serena swims 36 laps. She swims 9 laps of each stroke. How many different strokes does she swim?

Ron used $36 \div 9 = 4$ to solve the problem. What number sentence should Ron use to check his answer?

SOLUTION

1 See whether division or multiplication was used to solve the problem. Use the inverse operation to check the answer.

2 Find the inverse of the number sentence used to solve the problem.

ANSWER Division was used to solve the problem. Ron should use the inverse operation, multiplication. He should use the number sentence $4 \times 9 = 36$ to check his answer.

Write the number sentence that can be used to solve the problem. Then write the number sentence that can be used to check the answer.

4. Alexander solves 20 puzzles. He solves 5 puzzles each day. How many days does it take Alexander to solve the puzzles?

5. Rosa picked 54 flowers. She puts the same number of flowers into each of 6 baskets. How many flowers does she put into each basket?

6. Johnny practices his piano 6 hours each week. He has practiced 48 hours so far. How many weeks has Johnny been practicing the piano?

L E A R N

Use Inverse Relationships

Multiply or Divide and Check

Complete the fact family.

1. $8 \times 4 = \underline{?}$ $\underline{?} \times 8 = 32$ $\underline{?} \div \underline{?} = 4$ $32 \div 4 = \underline{?}$

Write the inverse multiplication fact.

2. $49 \div 7 = 7$

3. $15 \div 5 = 3$

Write a number sentence and solve the problem.
Then write a number sentence to check your work.

4. Colt had 24 blocks. He wanted to build a number of towers each 6 blocks tall. How many towers could he build?

5. Haley got a new video of cartoons. If the video has 8 cartoons and each cartoon is 3 minutes long, how long will the video play?

T R Y I T

Choose the answer.

6. Liza solved $18 \div 6 = ?$

Which fact can she use to check her answer?

A. $3 \times 6 = 18$

B. $15 + 3 = 18$

C. $21 - 3 = 18$

7. Oscar solved $6 \times 5 = ?$

Which fact can he use to check his answer?

A. $11 - 6 = 5$

B. $1 + 5 = 6$

C. $30 \div 5 = 6$

8. Matt read this problem.

Gary drives a total of 6 miles a day. How many miles will he drive in 3 days?

Matt used this number sentence to solve the problem.

$6 \times 3 = 18$

Which number sentence should Matt use to check his answer?

A. $18 \div 3 = ?$

B. $3 \div 18 = ?$

C. $6 \div 18 = ?$

D. $6 \div 3 = ?$

9. Oscar read this problem.

There are 10 apples in 1 box. How many apples are in 5 boxes?

Oscar used this number sentence to solve the problem.

$10 \times 5 = 50$

Which number sentence should Oscar use to check his answer?

A. $10 \div 50 = ?$

B. $50 \div 5 = ?$

C. $10 \div 5 = ?$

D. $5 \div 50 = ?$

T R Y   I T

Dividing with Remainders

Divide with Leftover Objects

Worked Examples

You can use objects or sketches to solve division story problems in which the objects do not divide evenly. What you do with the amount left over depends on what the story problem asks.

PROBLEM 1 A baker has 23 muffins and wants to place 4 in each box. How many boxes of 4 can the baker completely fill?

SOLUTION $23 \div 4 = ?$

Use circles to show 23 objects divided into groups of 4. You will have 5 complete groups and 3 objects left over.

$23 \div 4 = 5 \text{ r } 3$

Since the question asked how many boxes of 4 the baker can completely fill, the answer is 5. Ignore the 3 muffins left over.

ANSWER The baker can completely fill 5 boxes.

PROBLEM 2 A baker has 23 muffins and wants to place 4 in each box. How many muffins will be left over after he fills as many boxes of 4 as he can with the muffins?

SOLUTION $23 \div 4 = ?$

Use circles to show 23 objects divided into groups of 4. You will have 5 complete groups and 3 objects left over. Since the question asked how many muffins will be left over, the answer is 3.

$23 \div 4 = 5 \text{ r } 3$

ANSWER 3 muffins will be left over.

L E A R N

PROBLEM 3 A baker has 23 muffins and wants to place 4 in each box. How many boxes does he need if he is selling all 23 muffins?

SOLUTION $23 \div 4 = ?$

Use circles to show 23 objects divided into groups of 4. You will have 5 complete groups and 3 objects left over. Since the baker wants to sell all the muffins, he needs 5 boxes for the complete groups and a sixth box for the leftover muffins.

$23 \div 4 = 5 \text{ r } 3$

ANSWER The baker needs 6 boxes.

PROBLEM 4 A baker has 23 muffins and wants to place 4 in each box. How many boxes (including parts of boxes) can the baker fill?

SOLUTION $23 \div 4 = ?$

Use circles to show 23 objects divided into groups of 4. You will have 5 complete groups and 3 objects left over. Since the question asks how many boxes (including parts of boxes) the baker can fill, the answer is $5\frac{3}{4}$. The $\frac{3}{4}$ stands for the 3 muffins left over out of a group of 4.

$23 \div 4 = 5 \text{ r } 3$

ANSWER The baker can fill $5\frac{3}{4}$ boxes.

L E A R N

Use circles and this story problem to solve Problems 1–3.

The circus clown wants to share 10 balloons among 3 children. How many balloons would each child get?

1. How do you write the problem?

2. What should you do with the remainder?

3. What is the answer?

Use a sketch and this story problem to solve Problems 4–6.

The bakery donated 13 pies to the children's band to serve at the parties after their shows. If there are 2 shows, how many pies will be served after each show?

4. How do you write the problem?

5. What should you do with the remainder?

6. What is the answer?

Use a sketch or circles and this story problem to solve Problems 7–9.

The scout leader is renting buses to take 35 campers to the campsite. Each bus holds 10 campers. How many buses should the scout leader rent to take everyone on the camping trip?

7. How do you write the problem?

8. What should you do with the remainder?

9. What is the answer?

LEARN

Use a sketch or circles and this story problem to answer Problems 10–12.

Mr. Baker is arranging 45 muffins with 7 on each plate to take to the community breakfast. He decides that if there are any muffins left over, he will give them to his children. Will his children get any muffins? If yes, how many?

10. How do you write the problem?

11. What should you do with the remainder?

12. What is the answer?

Use a sketch or circles to answer the question.
Then explain your answer.

13. The chef has 15 sandwiches to separate equally on 3 platters. How many sandwiches will go on each platter?

14. The snack shop has 25 granola bars to share evenly among 4 people. How many granola bars will each person get?

15. There are 28 marbles in a bag. Each player needs 5 marbles to play a game. How many players can play?

16. The kennel has 26 doggie treats for 10 dogs to share evenly. The leftovers will be placed back in the jar. How many treats will go back in the jar?

LEARN

Dividing with Remainders

Division Story Problems

Answer the question. Be sure to use the remainder correctly.

1. There are 18 slices of watermelon to separate equally on 9 plates. How many slices of watermelon will be on each plate?

2. Henry found 22 shells at the beach. He wants to put exactly 5 shells into each bucket. How many buckets will have 5 shells?

Choose the answer.

3. Gordon has 24 grapes for his friends. He wants to give each person 6 grapes. Which sketch shows how many people Gordon can give grapes to?

A.
He can give grapes to 6 people.

B.
He can give grapes to 4 people.

C.
He can give grapes to 3 people.

D.
He can give grapes to 8 people.

4. Joel has 42 beads. He wants to sew 6 beads onto each shirt. Which sketch shows how many shirts Joel can sew beads onto?

A.
He can sew beads onto 6 shirts.

B.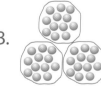
He can sew beads onto 3 shirts.

C.
He can sew beads onto 8 shirts.

D.
He can sew beads onto 7 shirts.

TRY IT

Divide Greater Numbers

Model and Record Multidigit Division

Worked Examples

You can use base-10 blocks to understand the standard algorithm for division.

PROBLEM $2\overline{)926}$

SOLUTION

① Write the problem on the Long Division – Hundreds printout.

② Start with the hundreds. Underline the 9. Divide the 9 hundreds flats evenly into 2 groups. There are 4 hundreds flats in each group. Write a 4 in the hundreds place of the quotient over the 9 to show that you put 4 hundreds in each group.

③ Think "4 hundreds times 2 is 8 hundreds, so 800 of the 926 blocks have been divided up." Subtract 800 from 926; there are 126 blocks left to divide.

$$
\begin{array}{c|c|c|c}
 & \text{Hundreds} & \text{Tens} & \text{Ones} \\
\hline
 & 4 & 6 & 3 \\
2\overline{)} & \underline{9} & 2 & 6 \\
- & 8 & 0 & 0 \\
\hline
 & 1 & 2 & 6 \\
\end{array}
$$

$400 \times 2 = 800$

④ Write 800 under 926 on the printout. Also write a minus symbol. Subtract.

⑤ Think "There are 126 blocks left to divide. Of that, there is 1 hundred. I can't put 1 hundred into 2 groups, so I have to break it into tens." Regroup the hundreds flat into 10 tens rods. Add those to the 2 tens you already have; that makes 12 tens.

L E A R N

6 Underline the 12 tens. Divide 12 tens by 2. The answer is 6 tens. Write a 6 in the tens place of the quotient on the printout.

```
        H T O
        4 6 3
    2 ) 9 2 6
      - 8 0 0     400 × 2 = 800
        1 2 6
      - 1 2 0     60 × 2 = 120
            6
```

7 6 tens times 2 is 12 tens or 60 times 2 equals 120, so you've divided up 120 more of out 926. Write 120 under the 126 on your printout. Subtract.

8 There are 6 ones left to divide. Divide the ones cubes into 2 groups; there are 3 in each group. Record the 3 in the ones column of the quotient. Think "3 ones times 2 is 6 ones." Write 6 in the ones column under the 6 at the bottom. Subtract to get zero. This shows you've divided up all the blocks. You can say this problem as "926 divided by 2 equals 463."

```
        H T O
        4 6 3
    2 ) 9 2 6
      - 8 0 0     400 × 2 = 800
        1 2 6
      - 1 2 0     60 × 2 = 120
            6
      -     6     3 × 2 = 6
            0
```

ANSWER

```
      463
  2 ) 926
```

LEARN

Copy these problems to the Long Division – Hundreds printout and solve.

1.

$$
\begin{array}{r}
\text{Hundreds} \quad \text{Tens} \quad \text{Ones} \\
1 \;?\;? \\
5\overline{)6\;7\;5} \\
-\;?\;?\;? \qquad 100 \times 5 = 500 \\
\overline{1\;7\;5} \\
-\;1\;5\;0 \qquad 30 \times 5 = 150 \\
\overline{\quad ?\;?} \\
-\quad ?\;? \qquad 5 \times 5 = 25 \\
\overline{\quad 0}
\end{array}
$$

2. $4\overline{)908}$

3. $2\overline{)726}$

LEARN

You can use a shortcut method to solve division problems. In this Worked Example, you will see the base-10 blocks shown, so that you can understand how the shortcut method actually works. This is the "behind the scenes" work. But, when you work the problems using the shortcut method, you can just picture the blocks in your head, if that helps you. All you need to do is write the problem worked out as shown in Step 3 of the Solution. The small number in the dividend shows the mental regrouping.

PROBLEM $2\overline{)726}$

SOLUTION

1 The base-10 blocks show 726 built with the fewest number of blocks possible.

2 Write the problem.

3 Divide the 7 hundreds by 2. There will be 3 hundreds in each group and 1 hundred left over. Write a 3 in the hundreds place of the quotient. Break up the remaining hundred into 10 tens. Record them in the tens place of the dividend. You now have 12 tens altogether. You write a little 1 up by the 2 in the dividend to show that you now have 12 tens.

300   300   12 tens

$$\begin{array}{r} 3 \\ 2\overline{)7^12\,6} \end{array}$$

4 Divide the 12 tens by 2. There will be 2 groups with 6 tens in each group. Write a 6 in the tens place of the quotient. There are no tens rods left over. There are only the 6 ones to divide by 2.

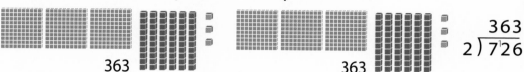

360   360   6 ones

$$\begin{array}{r} 36 \\ 2\overline{)7\overset{1}{2}6} \end{array}$$

5 Divide the 6 ones to make two groups with 3 in each group. Write a 3 in the ones place of the quotient.

363   363

$$\begin{array}{r} 363 \\ 2\overline{)7\overset{1}{2}6} \end{array}$$

ANSWER
$$\begin{array}{r} 363 \\ 2\overline{)726} \end{array}$$

LOOK BACK You can use the inverse operation, multiplication, to check the answer to the division problem.

$$\begin{array}{r} \overset{1}{3}63 \\ \times\ \ \ 2 \\ \hline 726 \end{array}$$

Solve using the shortcut method.

4. $2\overline{)722}$ 5. $3\overline{)372}$ 6. $5\overline{)805}$ 7. $4\overline{)628}$

L E A R N

Divide Greater Numbers

Record Division Practice

Solve.

1. $7\overline{)854}$

2. $4\overline{)972}$ $972 \div 4$

Choose the answer.

3. $238 \div 7 = ?$

   A. 54   B. 48   C. 43   D. 34

4. $495 \div 5 = ?$

   A. 109   B. 99   C. 90   D. 89

Solve.

5. $8\overline{)1{,}640}$

6. $3\overline{)1{,}350}$

7. $8\overline{)2{,}752}$

TRY IT

Story Problems with Equal Groups (A)
Use Long Division

Worked Examples

You can use long division or the shortcut method to solve a story problem that involves equal groups.

PROBLEM 1 The candle maker has 416 candles that need to be packed into boxes. Each box holds 8 candles. How many boxes does the candle maker need to pack all the candles?

SOLUTION 1 Long Division

1 Write the problem using the long-division symbol.

$$8\overline{)416}$$

2 Regroup the hundreds into tens. Underline the 4 and the 1 to help you remember that there are 41 tens.

$$8\overline{)\underline{41}6}$$

3 Divide the 41 tens by 8 to get 5 tens. Write the 5 in the tens place in the quotient.

$$8\overline{)416}^{\,5}$$

4 Multiply 5 tens times 8 or 50×8 to get 400. Write 400 below 416. Subtract.

$$\begin{array}{r} 5 \\ 8\overline{)416} \\ -400 \\ \hline 16 \end{array} \qquad 50 \times 8 = 400$$

5 There is 1 ten and 6 ones, or 16 ones, left to divide. Underline the 16. Divide 16 by 8 to get 2. Write the 2 in the ones place in the quotient. Multiply 2 ones times 8 to get 16. Write 16 below and subtract to get zero. There are no ones left to divide.

$$\begin{array}{r} 52 \\ 8\overline{)416} \\ -400 \\ \hline 16 \\ -16 \\ \hline 0 \end{array} \qquad 2 \times 8 = 16$$

L E A R N

SOLUTION 2 Shortcut Method

1 Write the problem. $8\overline{)416}$

2 Divide 41 tens by 8 to get 5 tens. Put a 5 in the tens place in the quotient.

3 Think "5 tens $\times$ 8 = 40 tens. So there's 1 ten left to divide."

4 Regroup the 1 ten and place a small 1 in the ones place to show that there are now 16 ones.

5 Divide 16 ones by 8 to get 2. Think "2 $\times$ 8 = 16 and there are none left over."

$$\begin{array}{r} 52 \\ 8\overline{)41^16} \end{array}$$

ANSWER 52; The candle maker will need 52 boxes to hold all the candles.

Use long division to solve the story problem.

1. The shirt factory has 1,461 buttons. If the workers put 3 buttons on each shirt, how many shirts can they make?

Use long division or the shortcut method of division to solve the story problem.

2. Serena has 260 postcards. She wants to put the same number of postcards in each of 4 albums. How many postcards can she put in each album?

LEARN

Story Problems with Equal Groups (A)

Solve Problems with Equal Groups

Solve.

1. Rosa has 738 songs in her library. She wants to make playlists with 9 songs in each. How many playlists can Rosa make?

2. The theater company made $3,647 selling tickets. If each ticket sold for $7, how many tickets were sold?

3. The farmer put 5 pumpkins into each box. He boxed 256 pumpkins in one month. How many complete boxes did he fill?

4. The 27 players on the baseball team are traveling to their game in cars. Each car can take 5 players. How many cars will be needed?

5. Colleen has 33 bagels. She wants to give 5 bagels to each person, and she wants to give bagels to as many people as possible. How many bagels will she have left over?

Challenge Question

Solve.

6. The florist has 2,005 roses. She makes bouquets with 5 roses in each. How many bouquets can she make?

T R Y   I T

Story Problems with Equal Groups (B)

Long Division with Remainders

Worked Examples

You can use division to solve a story problem that involves equal groups. You can use the problem to decide what to do with the remainder.

PROBLEM There are 124 rolls. The baker wants to put an equal number in each of 3 large baskets. How many rolls should she put in each basket?

SOLUTION Divide to solve the problem. Use the method that is easiest for you. One way is shown here.

1 Write the problem using the long-division symbol.

$$3\overline{)124}$$

2 Regroup the hundreds into tens. One hundred is equal to 10 tens.
Add the 10 tens to the 2 tens in the original dividend. You have 12 tens. Underline the 12 in the dividend.

$$3\overline{)\underline{12}4}$$

3 Divide the 12 tens by 3 to get 4 tens. Write the 4 in the tens place in the quotient.

$$3\overline{)\overset{4}{124}}$$

4 Multiply 4 tens times 3 or 40×3 to get 120. Write 120 below 124. Subtract.

$$\begin{array}{r} 4 \\ 3\overline{)124} \\ -120 \\ \hline 4 \end{array} \qquad 40 \times 3 = 120$$

L E A R N

5 There is 4 left to divide. Divide 4 by 3 to get 1. Write the 1 in the ones place in the quotient. Multiply 1 times 3 to get 3. Write 3 below 4, and subtract. There is 1 left to divide. This is the remainder. Write the remainder in the quotient.

$$
\begin{array}{r}
41\ \text{r}\,1 \\
3)\overline{124} \\
-120 \\
\hline
4 \\
-3 \\
\hline
1
\end{array}
\qquad
\begin{array}{l}
40 \times 3 = 120 \\[2mm]
1 \times 3 = 3
\end{array}
$$

6 Decide what to do with the remainder. Since 1 roll can be split into 3 pieces, you can write the remainder as a fraction. The remainder, 1, becomes the top number. The divisor (the number of people you're dividing by), 3, becomes the bottom number.

$$\frac{1}{3} \quad \begin{array}{l}\text{remainder}\\ \text{divisor}\end{array}$$

ANSWER The baker should put $41\frac{1}{3}$ rolls in each basket.

Solve. Use the story problem to decide what to do with the remainder.

1. There are 180 people attending a dinner party. Each table seats 8 people. How many tables are needed?

LEARN

Story Problems with Equal Groups (B)

Divide with Remainders

Answer the question.

1. Chef Ray is making 245 apple turnovers. He puts 9 turnovers on each pan to bake. How many pans does Chef Ray need?

2. What did you do with the remainder to answer the question in Problem 1?

3. Karla made 325 cookies. She filled tins with 7 cookies each. She put the leftover cookies on a plate. How many tins did Karla fill? How many cookies did she put on a plate?

4. The cooking class made 27 pies to share among 5 families. How many pies will each family get?

Choose the answer.

5. Nicole has 20 muffins. She gives each person 4 muffins. How many people can she give muffins to?

   A. 4   B. 5   C. 8   D. 16

Equal-Measure Story Problems

Divison at the Zoo

Worked Examples

Equal-measure problems have an amount that is used over and over to make a total. It could be a total distance; a total amount of money; a total amount of time; or a total amount of water, sand, or other material.

You can use division to solve many story problems involving equal measures.

PROBLEM Mr. Marshall has $130 to spend on tickets to the zoo. Tickets cost $9 each. How many tickets can Mr. Marshall buy?

SOLUTION

1 Figure out what you're being asked to find. The question asks how many $9 tickets Mr. Marshall can buy with $130.

2 Write the number sentence you can use to solve the problem.
$130 \div \$9 = ?$

3 Divide. $9)\overline{130}$ → $14\text{ r }4$

4 If there is a remainder, decide what to do with it. The question asks how many $9 tickets Mr. Marshall can buy; the remainder, $4, is not enough to buy a ticket, so ignore it.

ANSWER Mr. Marshall can buy 14 tickets.

L E A R N

Use this story problem to solve Problems 1–5.

A penguin swims 1,240 miles in a month. If the penguin swims
8 miles per hour, how many hours does it swim in a month?

1. What are you being asked to find?

2. What division number sentence can you use to solve
   the problem?

3. What is the answer to the division number sentence?

4. Is there a remainder? If so, what should you do with it?

5. What is the answer to the story problem?

Use this story problem to solve Problems 6–10.

The zoo feeds the animals 3,245 pounds of food in 5 days.
If the same amount of food is used each day, how many
pounds of food are used in a day?

6. What are you being asked to find?

7. What division number sentence can you use to solve
   the problem?

8. What is the answer to the division number sentence?

9. Is there a remainder? If so, what should you do with it?

10. What is the answer to the story problem?

Use this story problem to solve Problems 11–15.

The petting zoo had 150 ounces of grain to give to children to feed to the goats. The grain is stored in 8-ounce cups to give out to the children. How many cups are needed to store all the grain?

11. What are you being asked to find?

12. What division number sentence can you use to solve the problem?

13. What is the answer to the division number sentence?

14. Is there a remainder? If so, what should you do with it?

15. What is the answer to the story problem?

LEARN

Divide Money Amounts

Yard Sale Math

You can find the cost of a single item by dividing the total cost by the total number of items. (The items must all cost the same amount.)

PROBLEM 1 Rosa went to the store and bought 3 boxes of crayons for 75¢. How much does each box of crayons cost?

SOLUTION

1 Identify the total cost and the total number of items.
Total cost: 75¢
Total number of items: 3

2 Write a number sentence to divide the total cost by the total number of items.

$$75¢ \div 3 = ?$$

3 Divide.

```
       25¢
   3) 75¢
     −60
     ———
      15
     −15
     ———
       0
```

ANSWER Each box of crayons costs 25¢.

LEARN

PROBLEM 2 The store is having a sale on stencils. Rosa buys 4 stencils for 79¢. How much does one stencil cost?

SOLUTION

1 Identify the total cost and the total number of items.
Total cost: 79¢
Total number of items: 4

2 Write a number sentence to divide the total cost by the total number of items.

$79¢ \div 4 = ?$

3 Divide.

```
      19¢
  4) 79¢   r 3
    -40
     39
    -36
      3
```

4 This problem has a remainder. You cannot have a fraction of a cent. If you are finding the cost of an item and the quotient has a remainder, always make the cost the next greatest cent.

ANSWER One stencil costs 20¢.

L E A R N

Find the cost of one item.

PRICES
5 DOLLS FOR $25
3 CDS FOR $18
2 DRESSES FOR $16
6 SCARVES FOR $12
3 RINGS FOR 85¢
6 COMIC BOOKS FOR 98¢

YARD SALE

1. one CD

2. one doll

3. one scarf

4. one dress

5. one comic book

6. one ring

LEARN

Divide Money Amounts

Library Division

> **Worked Examples**
>
> You can find the cost of a single item by dividing the total cost by the total number of items. (The items must all cost the same amount.)
>
> **PROBLEM** A town is building a new library. The library committee bought 6 computers for $5,400. How much did each computer cost?
>
> **SOLUTION**
>
> **1** Identify the total cost and the total number of items.
>   Total cost: $5,400   Total number of items: 6
>
> **2** Write the problem using the long-division symbol.
>
> **3** Divide.
>
> $$\begin{array}{r} \$\ \ \ 900 \\ 6\overline{)\ \$\ 5,400} \end{array}$$
>
> $$\begin{array}{r} \$\ \ \ \ \ ? \\ 6\overline{)\$\ 5,400} \end{array}$$
>
> **ANSWER** Each computer cost $900.

Solve. All items in the problem have the same price.

1. The librarians bought 6 desks for $900. What was the cost of each desk?

2. The children picked out 8 bean bag chairs for the children's section. The total cost was $520. How much did each bean bag chair cost?

3. The parents bought the libray 3 digital cameras that the children could borrow. The total cost of the cameras was $2,550. What was the cost of each camera?

LEARN

Write Division Story Problems (A)

Division Story Examples

Worked Examples

You've learned about four types of division story problems:
- Sharing
- Dividing into equal groups
- Dividing into equal measures
- Finding the cost of a single item

PROBLEM Write a division story problem about finding the cost of a single item.

SOLUTION

1 Choose a theme. You could create a story problem about animals on a farm.

2 Choose something specific to write your problem about. You could write about the cost of food for the animals.

3 Decide specifically what quantities you want to write about. You could have the total cost of several bags of food and you could solve to find out how much each bag costs.

4 Choose numbers for each quantity. You could choose $192 for the total cost of 6 bags of food.

ANSWER A farmer buys food for the cows on his farm. He pays $192 for 6 bags of food. What is the cost of each bag of food?

Write the given type of division story problem.

1. sharing

2. dividing into equal groups

3. dividing into equal measures

You've learned about four ways to interpret a remainder when solving division story problems:

- Ignoring the remainder
- Using the remainder as the answer
- Increasing the answer by 1 because of the remainder
- Writing the remainder as a fraction of the divisor

PROBLEM There are 115 children waiting in line for a hayride. Each wagon holds 8 children. How many wagons are needed so that all the children can go on the hayride? Solve. Explain how you decided how to handle the remainder.

SOLUTION

1 Decide what the problem is asking. This problem is asking you to find how many wagons are needed so that all the children can go on the hayride.

2 Decide how you will solve the problem. To solve this problem, divide the number of children (115) by the number of children each wagon holds (8).

3 Write and solve a number sentence. $115 \div 8 = 14 \text{ r } 3$

4 Decide how to handle the remainder. The remainder in this problem represents 3 children. You know that *all* the children will be going on the hayride, so a wagon is needed for these 3 remaining children.

ANSWER 15 wagons are needed. Increase the answer by 1 because of the remainder.

L E A R N

Solve. Explain how you decided how to handle the remainder.

4. The farmer gathered 348 apples. He put 7 apples into each basket. He'll feed the leftover apples to his pigs. How many apples will the farmer feed to his pigs?

5. The farm produced 1,000 pounds of grain. The farmer will divide the grain among 3 silos. How much grain will the farmer put in each silo?

6. The cows on the farm produced enough milk to fill 267 bottles. The farmer is going to sell the milk at 5 farmer's markets. He wants to bring an equal number of bottles to each market. How many bottles can he bring to each market?

7. Write a division story problem that has a remainder. Then solve the problem and explain how you handled the remainder.

8. Write a division story problem that has a remainder that is handled differently from the remainder in Problem 7. Then solve the problem and explain how you handled the remainder.

LEARN

Use the Order of Operations

Practice Finding the Value

Memory Jogger

ORDER OF OPERATIONS

Multiply or divide from left to right in the order that the $\times$ or $\div$ symbols appear. Then add or subtract from left to right in the order that the $+$ or $-$ symbols appear.

$$5 + 3 \times 6 \div 2$$
$$\vee$$
$$5 + 18 \div 2$$
$$\vee$$
$$5 + 9 = 14$$

$$48 \div 6 - 2 \times 3$$
$$\vee$$
$$8 - 2 \times 3$$
$$\vee$$
$$8 - 6 = 2$$

Find the value.

1. $9 + 12 \div 3 \times 5$

2. $25 - 8 \times 2 + 1$

3. $32 - 18 \div 6 + 3 \times 9$

4. $50 - 17 + 11$

5. $25 - 3 + 5$

6. $12 - 5 \times 2$

7. $16 - 3 \times 5$

8. $15 - 5 \times 2 + 1$

9. $10 \times 5 - 4 + 1$

10. $18 - 9 \div 3 + 4$

11. $55 - 15 \div 5 + 10$

12. $48 \div 6 + 2$

13. $36 \div 9 - 3$

14. $4 \div 2 + 6 \times 6$

15. $20 \div 4 - 2 \times 2$

Challenge Question

Solve.

16. Write an expression that uses all four operations and has a value of 24.

T R Y I T

Choose the Correct Operation (A)

Add or Subtract to Solve

Worked Examples

Asking yourself problem-solving questions can help you work through addition and subtraction story problems.

PROBLEM A total of 1,984 people visited the park on Thursday. There were 1,237 children and the rest were adults. How many adults visited the park on Thursday? Tell which operation to use to solve the problem. Then solve.

SOLUTION Ask yourself the following questions:
- What are you asked to find in the story problem?
- Would a picture or model help you understand the problem?
- Which operation will you use?
- How do you know that you should use that operation?
- What number sentence will you use to solve the story problem?

Find the difference between the total and one part. Draw a chart to help you understand the problem.

1,984 people	
1,237 children	? adults

Subtract to find the answer. $1,984 - 1,237 = 747$

ANSWER There were 747 adults who visited the park on Thursday.

LEARN

Tell which operation to use to solve the problem. Then solve.

1. On Friday, 2,756 people were at the park. When it started to rain, 1,284 people left.

   How many people were still at the park?

2. On Saturday, 3,245 people visited the amusement park. On Sunday, 2,876 people visited the park.

   How many people visited the park over the weekend?

3. At the popcorn stand, 765 bags of buttered popcorn and 592 bags of caramel popcorn were sold.

   How many bags of popcorn were sold in all?

4. There were 852 people who rode the Ferris wheel and 975 people who rode the carousel.

   How many more people rode the carousel than the Ferris wheel?

5. There were 173 tickets sold for the bumper cars in the morning and 58 tickets sold in the afternoon.

   How many tickets in all were sold for the bumper cars?

LEARN

Choose the Correct Operation (A)

Multiply or Divide to Solve

Worked Examples

Asking yourself problem-solving questions can help you work through multiplication and division story problems.

PROBLEM A quilt has 12 squares in each row. There are 9 rows. How many squares are in the quilt altogether? Tell which operation to use to solve the problem. Then solve.

SOLUTION Ask yourself the following questions:
- What are you asked to find in the story problem?
- Would a picture or model help you understand the problem?
- Which operation will you use?
- How do you know that you should use that operation?
- What number sentence will you use to solve the story problem?

Find the total number of squares. Combine equal groups, so multiply. $9 \times 12 = 108$

ANSWER There are 108 squares in the quilt.

Tell which operation to use to solve the problem. Then solve.

1. There are 258 paintbrushes. If 6 brushes are sold each day, in how many days will all the paintbrushes be sold?

2. Lauren buys 8 vases. Each vase costs $4.

   How much does Lauren spend?

LEARN

3. Ellen and her 2 brothers share 129 star stickers equally.

How many stickers do Ellen and each of her brothers get?

4. The knitting class made 5 scarves every day for a week.

How many scarves did they make in all?
(**Hint:** 1 week = 7 days)

5. Mr. Getty paid his workers $672. If each of the 4 workers was paid the same amount, how much did each worker earn?

LEARN

Choose the Correct Operation (B)

Explain Thinking About Solutions

Worked Examples

You can use problem-solving questions to help you solve story problems that involve addition, subtraction, multiplication, and division.

PROBLEM Serena paid $18 for 6 sheets of poster paper. What is the cost of 1 sheet of poster paper? Tell which operation to use to solve the problem. Then solve.

SOLUTION You need to find the cost of 1 sheet of poster paper. You don't need a picture or model to solve the problem; just use the numbers. You know the total amount and you need to find the cost of 1 item. Use division to solve the problem. Use the number sentence $18 \div 6 = ?$ to find the answer.

ANSWER $18 \div 6 = 3; One sheet of poster paper costs $3.

Tell which operation to use to solve the problem. Then solve.

1. So far this year, Alexander has solved 102 puzzles. Last year, he solved 273 puzzles.

   How many more puzzles does Alexander need to solve this year to match the number of puzzles he solved last year?

2. Johnny practices piano for 45 minutes a week.

   How many minutes will he practice in 6 weeks?

3. Rosa has 145 songs from musicals in her playlist. She has 97 other songs.

   How many songs does Rosa have in her playlist altogether?

Choose the Correct Operation (B)
Solve Circus Story Problems

Worked Examples

You can use problem-solving questions to help you solve story problems that involve addition, subtraction, multiplication, and division.

PROBLEM There are 6 circus shows. For each show, there are 1,250 tickets sold. How many tickets are sold for the circus shows in all? Tell which operation to use to solve the problem. Then solve.

SOLUTION The story problem asks how many tickets in all are sold. You know that 1,250 tickets are sold for each show and there are 6 shows. This problem is asking you to combine the 6 equal groups of 1,250 tickets. Multiply 6 by 1,250 to get the answer. Write a sentence labeling the answer with "tickets" because the problem asks "how many tickets."

$$
\begin{array}{r}
1\ 3 \\
1{,}250 \\
\times6 \\
\hline
7{,}500
\end{array}
$$

ANSWER $6 \times 1{,}250 = 7{,}500$; In all, 7,500 tickets are sold.

LEARN

Tell which operation to use to solve the problem. Then solve.

1. On Saturday, there were 4,368 people at the circus.
   On Sunday, there were 3,782 people at the circus.

   How many more people were at the circus on Saturday than on Sunday?

2. There were 5,421 advance tickets sold and 1,738 tickets sold at the door.

   How many tickets were sold altogether?

3. The cost for 8 bales of hay for the circus horses is $96.

   What is the cost for a bale of hay?

Choose the Correct Operation (B)

Choose the Operation at Camp

Write the number sentence to solve the problem. Then solve.

1. There were 3,076 campers in July. There were 2,851 campers in August.

   How many campers were there altogether?

2. Ron hiked 4 miles each of the 14 days he was at camp.

   How many total miles did Ron hike while at camp?

3. Visors cost $7 each at the camp store. A total of $5,761 was made selling visors.

   How many visors did the store sell?

4. At the beginning of the summer, there were 950 songbooks. At the end of the summer, there were 786 songbooks.

   How many songbooks were lost or damaged during the summer?

Challenge Question

Write the number sentence to solve the problem. Then solve. Explain your solution.

5. A group of 35 campers went to the lake to go canoeing. Campers could decide if they wanted 2 or 3 people in their canoes. (They weren't allowed to have any canoes with only 1 person.) How many canoes did they need? (**Hint:** Find the least number of canoes they could use and the greatest number of canoes they could use.)

T R Y   I T

Use More Than One Operation (A)

Problems with More Than One Step

Worked Examples

You can solve story problems with two or more operations.

PROBLEM Stella has 2 bags of marbles. There are 6 marbles in each bag. She gets 4 more marbles.

How many marbles does she have in all?

SOLUTION Ask yourself the following questions:
- What are you asked to find in the problem?
- What facts are given?
- Would a picture or model help you understand the problem?
- How are you going to solve the problem?
- Do you need to use more than one operation in this problem?
- What are the different steps you need to take to solve this problem?
- Which operations should you use? Why?

You need to find how many marbles Stella has in all. She starts with some marbles (2 bags of 6 marbles) and then gets more (4). Multiply $2 \times 6 = 12$ to find how many marbles she has at the beginning. Then add the marbles she gets to find the total number of marbles. $12 + 4 = 16$

ANSWER $2 \times 6 = 12$; $12 + 4 = 16$; Stella has 16 marbles in all.

L E A R N

Solve.

1. Brian and Kelly are 8 years old. Each bought an admission pass to the zoo for $6 and a box of animal crackers for $3.

    How much money did they spend in all?

2. There are 2 boxes of chalk and 8 pieces of chalk in each box.

    If there are 4 children drawing with chalk, how many pieces of chalk will each child get?

3. Ed bought 3 cartons of eggs at the store. There are 18 eggs in each carton. He also bought a carton of 6 eggs.

    How many eggs does Ed have altogether?

4. There are 3 birds' nests in the tree. Each nest had 5 eggs.

    If 3 eggs have already hatched, how many eggs are left still to hatch?

LEARN

Use More Than One Operation (B)

Problem-Solving Questions

Worked Examples

You can break down story problems into steps to find a solution. You can choose the operation for each step to answer the question.

PROBLEM Sam buys 316 pounds of food for the elephants from one store and 950 pounds of food from another store.
He needs to put the same amount of food into each of 3 bins.

How many pounds of food will Sam put into each bin?

SOLUTION You need to find out how much food Sam will put into each bin. First figure out how much food Sam has altogether. You know he bought 316 pounds at one store and 950 at another. Add $316 + 950 = 1,266$. Sam will put the same amount into each of 3 bins, so divide the total, 1,266, by 3. $1,266 \div 3 = 422$

ANSWER $316 + 950 = 1,266$; $1,266 \div 3 = 422$; Sam will put 422 pounds of food into each bin.

Solve.

1. Tina, a tightrope walker, buys a spool of wire that is 60 feet long and a spool of wire that is 45 feet long. She uses the wire to make 7 equal-length tightropes. How long is each tightrope?

2. A juggler has 5 bags of juggling pins. There are 6 pins in each bag. Each pin weighs 7 ounces. What is the total weight of all the juggling pins?

3. There are 25 clowns in the first act and 47 additional clowns in the second act. If 8 clowns fit in 1 clown car, how many clown cars are needed to fit all the clowns?

Use More Than One Operation (B)

More Than One Operation

Solve.

1. At the circus, Mr. Smith buys cotton candy for $3 and 2 drinks for $2 each. He gives the cashier $10.

   How much change does Mr. Smith receive?

2. A clown is carrying 17 red balloons, 24 blue balloons, and 12 yellow balloons. She gives away 38 balloons to children.

   How many balloons does the clown have left?

3. There are 27 girl clowns and 39 boy clowns. An equal number of clowns squeeze into each of 6 clown cars.

   How many clowns are in each car?

4. David goes to the circus with 2 friends and 3 cousins. His parents give him $90 to share equally with his friends and cousins.

   How much money does each person get?

5. The circus is moving to the next city. The circus train travels a total of 517 miles in three days. The train travels 208 miles the first day and 173 miles the second day.

   How many miles does the circus train travel on the third day?

6. Lisa raised $1,934 with her car wash, and Gary raised $2,560 with his auction. They spent $300 on advertising.

   How much money did they have after paying for the advertising?

TRY IT

7. Ivan went fishing with his dad. His dad caught 8 fish, and Ivan caught 14 fish. They brought home 5 fish and threw the rest back into the water.

   How many fish did they throw back into the water?

8. Charlie had three $5 bills and four $10 bills in his wallet. He spent $23 on dinner.

   How much does Charlie have left?

9. The dairy farm has 22 brown cows and 18 spotted cows. Each brown cow produces 9 gallons of milk a day, and each spotted cow produces 8 gallons of milk a day.

   How much milk can the dairy farm produce in a day?

Challenge Question

Solve.

10. The circus animal trainer is preparing to leave town. Before he leaves, the trainer has to buy more food for the animals. He buys 893 pounds of food at the Circus Food Store. Then he buys 457 pounds of food from Circus Animal Treat Shop. The trainer stores the food in 9 crates. Each crate holds the same amount of food.

    How many pounds of food are in each crate?

TRY IT

Identify and Classify Polygons

Name Polygons

Write the name of the polygon.

1.

2.

3.

4.

5.

6.

7.

8.

T R Y   I T

Choose the answer.

9. Which is a pentagon?

A.    B.

C.    D.

10. Which is a pentagon?

A.    B.

C.   D.

11. Which sign is in the shape of an octagon?

A.   B.

C.   D.

12. Which placemat is in the shape of an quadrilateral?

A.    B.

C.    D.

13. What is the name of this figure?

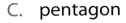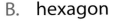

A. hexagon
B. pentagon
C. octagon
D. quadrilateral

14. What is the name of this figure?

A. octagon
B. hexagon
C. pentagon
D. triangle

15. How many sides does a quadrilateral have?

A. 3   B. 4
C. 5   D. 6

16. How many sides does a rectangle have?

A. 3   B. 4
C. 5   D. 8

Read the problem and follow the directions.

17. Use dot paper to draw a design of your choice. When you have finished, name the polygons that are in the design.

Parallelograms

Parallelogram Practice

Describe the shape. Use dot paper to draw an example.

1. parallelogram
2. rectangle
3. square

Read the statement. Tell whether it is true or false.

4. All parallelograms are squares.
5. All squares are rectangles.
6. All rectangles are parallelograms.

Choose the answer.

7. Which best describes all rectangles?

    A. Opposite sides are perpendicular.

    B. All sides are the same length.

    C. They have 4 right angles.

8. Which best describes all parallelograms?

    A. Opposite sides are parallel.

    B. All sides are the same length.

    C. They have 2 right angles and 2 angles that are greater than a right angle.

9. Which is the length of the fourth side of this rectangle?

    A. 4 cm

    B. 5 cm

    C. 7 cm

    D. 10 cm

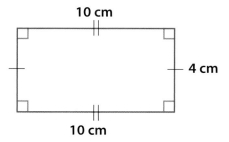

TRY IT

10. Which is the length of the fourth side of this square?

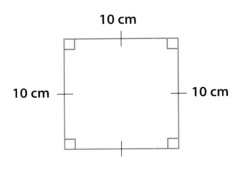

A. 2 cm

B. 5 cm

C. 10 cm

D. 12 cm

11. Choose **two** words that correctly name this shape.

A. parallelogram

B. quadrilateral

C. rectangle

12. Choose **two** words that correctly name this shape.

A. square

B. rectangle

C. quadrilateral

TRY IT

Identify and Classify Solids

Attributes of Solids

Worked Examples

You can count the faces, edges, curved surfaces, and vertices of solids.

PROBLEM 1 How many faces, edges, curved surfaces, and vertices does a cube have?

SOLUTION

1. Faces are flat surfaces. The cube has 6 flat surfaces.

2. Edges are where faces meet. The cube has 12 edges.

3. Curved surfaces are not flat. The cube does not have any curved surfaces.

4. Vertices are corners. The cube has 8 vertices.

ANSWER The cube has 6 faces, 12 edges, 0 curved surfaces, and 8 vertices.

PROBLEM 2 How many faces, edges, curved surfaces, and vertices does a sphere have?

SOLUTION

1. Faces are flat surfaces. The sphere does not have any flat surfaces.

2. Edges are where faces meet. The sphere does not have any edges.

3. Curved surfaces are not flat. The sphere has 1 curved surface.

4. Vertices are corners. The sphere does not have any vertices.

ANSWER The sphere has 0 flat surfaces, 0 edges, 1 curved surface, and 0 vertices.

L E A R N

Write the missing numbers of faces, edges, curved surfaces, and vertices.

	Solids	Faces	Edges	Curved Surfaces	Vertices
1.	cone	1	1	1	?
2.	cylinder	2	?	?	?
3.	sphere	0	?	?	?
4.	rectangular prism	?	?	?	?
5.	cube	?	?	?	?
6.	square pyramid	?	?	?	?
7.	triangular pyramid	?	?	?	?

LEARN

Identify and Classify Solids

Classify Solids

Name the solid. Use the words in the box to help with spelling.

square pyramid	cube	cylinder
triangular pyramid	cone	sphere
rectangular prism		

1.

2.

3.

4.

5.

6.

7.

Choose the answer or answers.

8. Which figures are cubes? Choose more than one.

   A.   B.    C.    D.

9. Which figures are cones? Choose more than one.

   A.   B.   C.   D.

159

TRY IT

10. Which figures are spheres? Choose more than one.

A.   B.   C.   D.

11. Which objects are prisms? Choose more than one.

A.   B.    C.   D.

12. Which figure is a cylinder?

A.   B.   C.   D.

13. Which figure can have 6 faces all the same size and shape?

A. cylinder   B. cone   C. pyramid   D. cube

Answer the question.

14. How many faces does this prism have?

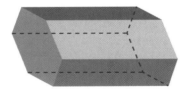

15. How many vertices does this pyramid have?

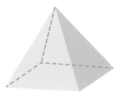

16. How many edges does this pyramid have?

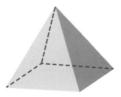

T R Y   I T

Combine Solids to Create New Shapes

Together and Apart

Match the solids to the objects they make when combined.

1.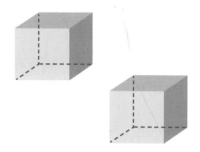

A.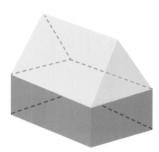

2.

B.

3.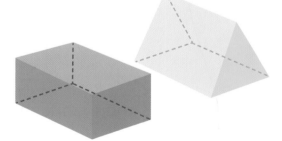

C.

Name the solids that were combined to create the object.

4.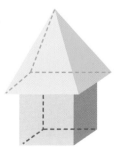

5.

TRY IT

Which shapes were combined to make the object? Choose the answer.

6.

A. sphere and cylinder

B. sphere and cone

C. cone and prism

D. prism and cylinder

7.

A. sphere and pyramid

B. pyramid and prism

C. two prisms

D. two pyramids

8.

A. two cubes

B. two pyramids

C. two prisms

D. two cylinders

9.

A. prism and sphere

B. sphere and cylinder

C. sphere and pyramid

D. sphere and cube

TRY IT

Decimal Place Values

Place and Value of Decimal Numbers

Choose the answer.

1. Which number has a 6 in the tenths place?

   A. 50.06   B. 58.6

   C. 63.589   D. 73.536

2. Which number has a 3 in the hundredths place?

   A. 286.63   B. 386.72

   C. 472.123   D. 521.38

3. Which number has a 4 in the thousandths place?

   A. 38.84   B. 56.234

   C. 183.432   D. 4,195.38

4. Which digit is in the hundredths place in the number 2,758.492?

   A. 2   B. 4

   C. 7   D. 9

5. Which digit is in the tenths place in the number 854.397?

   A. 3   B. 4

   C. 5   D. 9

6. Which shows 8 thousandths written as a decimal?

   A. 0.008   B. 0.08

   C. 0.8   D. 8,000.0

Answer the question.

7. Which digit is in the tenths place in the number 469.283?

8. Which digit is in the hundredths place in the number 1,207.639?

Write the place value of the digit 4 in the number.

9. 5.426   10. 3.954   11. 4.267   12. 0.348

Write the value of the digit 8 in the number.

13. 0.985   14. 2.832   15. 1.008

TRY IT

Money in Decimal Notation

Add or Subtract Money Amounts

You can solve addition and subtraction story problems with decimal numbers by lining up the place values and adding or subtracting.

PROBLEM 1 Sam has $4.26. He gets $2.53 more. How much money does Sam have now?

SOLUTION

1 Write the numbers vertically. Make sure to line up numbers of the same place value. Remember to include the dollar symbols and the plus symbol.

$$\begin{array}{r} \$\,4.26 \\ +\ \$\,2.53 \\ \hline \end{array}$$

2 Add the pennies (hundredths), dimes (tenths), and $1 bills (ones) from right to left. Remember to regroup when needed. Remember to include the dollar symbol.

$$\begin{array}{r} \$\,4.26 \\ +\ \$\,2.53 \\ \hline \$\,6.79 \end{array}$$

ANSWER Sam now has $6.79.

LEARN

PROBLEM 2 Judy's scout troop held a car wash. The scouts raised $98.76. They spent $12.34 of that money on a new troop banner. How much money did they have left?

SOLUTION

1 Write the numbers vertically. Make sure to line up numbers of the same place value. Remember to include the dollar symbols and the minus symbol.

$$\begin{array}{r} \$\ 98.76 \\ -\ \$\ 12.34 \\ \hline \end{array}$$

2 Subtract the pennies (hundredths), dimes (tenths), and $1 bills (ones) from right to left. Remember to regroup when needed. Remember to include the dollar symbol.

$$\begin{array}{r} \$\ 98.76 \\ -\ \$\ 12.34 \\ \hline \$\ 86.42 \end{array}$$

ANSWER The scouts had $86.42 left.

Solve.

1. Leila is at the movies. She buys a hot dog for $5.87 and popcorn for $3.38. How much money does she spend altogether?

2. Martin goes to the store with $26.39. He buys a box of cereal for $2.48. How much money does he have left?

L E A R N

Money in Decimal Notation

Solve Money Story Problems

Solve.

1. Ava is at the store with $16.00. She buys a new doll for $12.75. How much money does Ava have left?

2. Thomas worked as a pet sitter for three weeks. He earned $15.50, $10.75, and $20.25. How much money did Thomas earn in all?

Choose the answer.

3. Carlos bought a notebook for $3.24, a pencil for $1.79, and an eraser for $2.23. What was the total cost of these three items?

   A. $6.26   B. $6.16   C. $7.16   D. $7.26

4. Manuel bought toothpaste for $5.49 and a toothbrush for $2.99. What was the total cost of the two items?

   A. $2.50   B. $7.38   C. $8.38   D. $8.48

5. Jia bought a frame for $19.44 and a piece of art for $24.75. What was the cost of the two items?

   A. $44.19   B. $43.19   C. $33.19   D. $5.31

6. Cari bought a ball for $2.49. She gave the cashier $3.00. How much money did she get back?

   A. $0.51   B. $0.61   C. $1.49   D. $5.49

TRY IT

Money Story Problems (A)

Aquarium Story Problems

Worked Examples

You can use multiplication to solve some story problems involving decimals and money.

PROBLEM Tickets for the aquarium cost $23.95 each. Mrs. Jackson bought 4 aquarium tickets.
What was the total cost for the tickets?

SOLUTION Multiply 4 × $23.95 to find the cost of 4 tickets. Multiply from right to left.

1 Multiply the hundredths. 4 times 5 hundredths is 20 hundredths. 20 hundredths is regrouped as 2 tenths 0 hundredths, just as 20 pennies can be regrouped into 2 dimes and 0 pennies. (Be sure to record the 2 regrouped dimes in the tenths place at the top and the 0 pennies in the hundredths place of the answer.)

2 Multiply the tenths. 4 times 9 tenths is 36 tenths or 36 dimes. Add the 2 regrouped dimes to get 38 dimes. 38 dimes is regrouped as 3 $1 dollar bills and 8 dimes.

3 Multiply the ones. 4 times 3 ones is 12 ones. Add the regrouped 3 ones to get 15 ones. 15 ones is regrouped as 1 ten and 5 ones.

4 Multiply the tens. 4 times 2 tens is 8 tens. Add the regrouped 1 ten to get 9 tens.

$$
\begin{array}{r}
\overset{\text{tens (\$10 bills)}}{} \overset{\text{ones (\$1 bills)}}{} . \overset{\text{tenths (dimes)}}{} \overset{\text{hundredths (pennies)}}{} \\
1\ 3\quad 2 \\
\$23.95 \\
\times4 \\
\hline
\$95.80
\end{array}
$$

L E A R N

5 Remember to place the decimal point between the tenths and the ones and write the dollar symbol in the answer.

ANSWER The total cost was $95.80 for 4 tickets.

Solve.

1. Kylie and her 5 friends want to see the dolphin show at the aquarium. Each dolphin-show ticket costs $3.75.

   What is the price for 6 dolphin-show tickets?

2. The aquarium gift shop sells T-shirts for $15.25.

   How much will 9 T-shirts cost?

3. Malia bought 7 postcards at the aquarium. Each postcard cost $0.89.

   How much did Malia spend on the postcards?

4. A hotel near the aquarium charges $119.37 a night.

   How much will it cost to stay at the hotel for 3 nights?

LEARN

Money Story Problems (A)

Money Stories and Multiplication

Solve.

1. Tina bought 3 cat toys at the pet store. Each cat toy cost $4.67. How much did Tina spend on cat toys?

2. The pet store is having a sale on large bags of dog food. 1 large bag costs $21.85. What is the cost for 5 large bags of dog food?

3. Sophie bought 6 kitchen chairs. Each chair cost $48.79. How much did Sophie spend on chairs?

Choose the answer.

4. Mira bought 7 oranges. Each orange cost $0.49. How much did Mira spend on oranges?

   A. $0.07   B. $0.70   C. $2.83   D. $3.43

TRY IT

Money Story Problems (B)

Zoo Story Problems

Worked Examples

You can use division to solve some story problems involving decimals and money.

PROBLEM Mr. Roth buys 5 tickets to the zoo. Each ticket costs the same amount. He spends a total of $59.75. How much does each ticket cost?

SOLUTION Divide $59.75 by 5 to find the cost of each ticket. Divide, starting with the greatest place value and moving left to right from the tens to the ones, then the tenths, and finally the hundredths.

1 Divide the tens. 5 tens divided by 5 is 1 ten. Record the 1 in the tens place. There are no tens left over.

2 Divide the ones. 9 ones divided by 5 is 1, with 4 ones left over. Record the 1 in the ones place. Regroup the 4 ones as 40 tenths. Show the 40 tenths with a small 4 in the tenths place. There are now 47 tenths.

3 Place the decimal point between the ones place and the tenths place in the answer.

4 Divide the tenths. 47 tenths divided by 5 is 9, with 2 tenths left over. Record the 9 in the tenths place. Regroup the 2 tenths as 20 hundredths. Show the 20 hundredths with a small 2 in the hundredths place. There are now 25 hundredths.

5 Divide the hundredths. 25 hundredths divided by 5 is 5 hundredths with no hundredths left over. Record the 5 in the hundredths place. Write the dollar symbol in the answer.

ANSWER Each ticket costs $11.95.

Solve.

1. 4 friends have a total of $48.60 to spend at the zoo. If they share the money equally, how much will each person get?

2. Erin bought 3 animal plush toys at the zoo gift shop. She spent a total of $21.45. Each animal plush toy was the same price. What is the price of 1 animal plush toy?

3. Mr. Roth and his family stayed at the hotel near the zoo. The total cost for their 3-night stay was $391.53. What was the cost for 1 night?

LEARN

Money Story Problems (B)

Money Stories and Division

Solve.

1. Monique rented a bike for $15.99 for 3 hours. How much did Monique spend for each hour?

2. The soccer team paid $247.26 for 6 new uniforms. How much did each uniform cost?

Choose the answer.

3. Alexander spent a total of $64.26 for 6 identical bunches of flowers. How much did each bunch of flowers cost?

   A. $1.71   B. $10.71   C. $17.10   D. $385.56

4. Walter rented a car for $875.25 for 9 days. How much did the car cost each day?

   A. $97.25   B. $97.50   C. $7,235.85   D. $62.87

TRY IT

Money Story Problems (C)

Art Club Story Problems

Worked Examples

You can solve two-step problems using multiplication and division with money amounts.

PROBLEM The art club wanted to buy 5 jars of paint at $3.27 a jar. Three members of the club said they would share the cost. How much did each person have to pay?

SOLUTION Break down the problem into steps and solve each step.

1 Multiply to find the total cost of 5 jars of paint at $3.27 each.

$$
\begin{array}{r}
\overset{1\ 3}{\$\ 3.27} \\
\times\ \ \ \ \ 5 \\
\hline
\$16.35
\end{array}
$$

2 Divide the total cost by 3 to see how much each person had to pay.

$$
\begin{array}{r}
\$\ 5.45 \\
3\overline{)\,\$16.\overset{1\ 1}{3}5}
\end{array}
$$

ANSWER Each person had to pay $5.45.

Solve.

1. Mr. Mathews ordered 8 boxes of markers for $3.25 each and a package of construction paper for $5.70. What was the total amount of his order?

2. Lisa spent a total of $46.00 at the art store. She bought a set of colored pencils for $31.60 and spent the rest on 6 tubes of glue. How much did each tube of glue cost?

L E A R N

Money Story Problems (C)

Money Stories

Solve.

1. Jazmyne buys 5 pounds of apples for $1.89 a pound and a watermelon for $7.49. How much does Jazmyne spend on fruit?

2. Christine bought 4 hair clips and 3 hair bands.
Each hair clip cost $0.28. Each hair band cost $0.93.
How much did Christine spend altogether?

Choose the answer.

3. James bought 4 pairs of socks and 3 shirts.
Each pair of socks cost $3.45. Each shirt cost $25.56.
How much did James spend altogether?

   A. $29.01   B. $90.48   C. $112.59   D. $203.07

TRY IT

Represent and Name Fractions (A)

Name Fractions

Match the sketch to its fraction name.

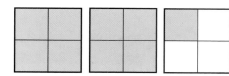

$$\frac{6}{7} \qquad \frac{8}{5}$$

$$1\frac{2}{3} \qquad\qquad 2\frac{1}{4}$$

$$\frac{2}{3} \qquad\qquad \frac{7}{8}$$

1.

1 whole

2.

1 whole

3.

4.
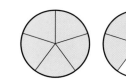

5.

6.

1 whole

Choose the answer.

7. Jeff said that this model shows $2\frac{3}{8}$ shaded.

Eliza said that this model shows $\frac{19}{8}$ shaded. Who is correct?

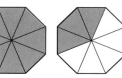
1 whole

A. Jeff

B. Eliza

C. both Jeff and Eliza

T R Y   I T

8. Which model shows $\frac{1}{3}$ shaded?

A.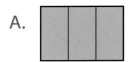

B.

C.

D.

9. Which model shows $1\frac{3}{4}$ shaded?

A.

B.

C.

D.

10. What fraction of the figure is shaded?

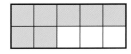

A. $\frac{3}{7}$ B. $\frac{7}{3}$ C. $\frac{7}{7}$ D. $\frac{7}{10}$

11. What fraction of the set is made up of triangles?

A. $\frac{4}{5}$ B. $\frac{5}{9}$ C. $\frac{9}{5}$ D. $\frac{5}{5}$

12. Which mixed number is represented using this diagram?

1 whole

A. $\frac{11}{12}$ B. $1\frac{5}{6}$ C. $1\frac{6}{5}$ D. $1\frac{11}{12}$

TRY IT

13. Which mixed number is represented using this diagram?

1 whole

A. $1\frac{8}{16}$ B. $3\frac{5}{8}$ C. $\frac{16}{8}$ D. $3\frac{8}{5}$

14. Which improper fraction is represented using this diagram?

1 whole

A. $\frac{5}{4}$ B. $\frac{29}{8}$ C. $\frac{8}{4}$ D. $\frac{16}{8}$

T R Y   I T

Represent and Name Fractions (B)

Represent Fractions

You can sketch a fraction three ways—as part of a whole, as part of a set, and as a number on a number line.

SKETCH $\frac{1}{4}$

Part of a whole	
Part of a set	
A number on a number line	

Sketch the fraction three ways—as part of a whole, as part of a set, and as a number on a number line. Use the chart above to help you.

1. $\frac{2}{5}$

2. $\frac{3}{8}$

Read the problem and follow the directions.

3. Show this model on a number line.

4. Sketch $4\frac{3}{4}$ as a model of part of a whole with rectangles, as a mixed number on a number line, and as an improper fraction on a number line.

TRY IT

5. Laine said that only three of these models show $1\frac{1}{4}$.
Is Laine correct? Explain your answer.

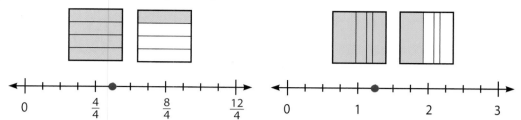

Choose the answer.

6. Rea said this model shows $2\frac{3}{4}$ shaded. Donna said this
model shows $\frac{13}{4}$ shaded. Who is correct?

   A. Rea

   B. Donna

   C. both Rea and Donna

7. Which model does **not** show $\frac{9}{12}$?

A.

B.

C.

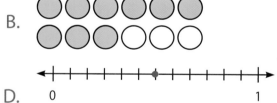

D.

8. Which model shows $\frac{3}{4}$ shaded?

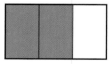

A.

B.

C.

D.

T R Y   I T

9. Which number line shows the location of the mixed number shown in this model?

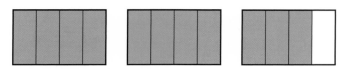

A.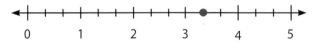
   0   1   2   3   4

B.
   0   1   2   3   4

C.
   0   1   2   3   4

D.
   0   1   2   3   4

10. Which sketch shows the same fraction that is shown on this number line?

   0   1   2   3   4   5

A.

B.

C.

D.

TRY IT

11. What fraction of the figure is shaded?

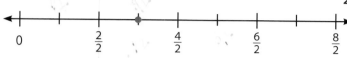

A. $\frac{5}{12}$ B. $\frac{12}{12}$ C. $\frac{7}{12}$ D. $\frac{12}{7}$

12. Phil said that both of these models show $\frac{3}{2}$.

A. Phil is correct.

B. Phil is not correct because the number line shows $2\frac{1}{2}$.

C. Phil is not correct because the model shows $2\frac{1}{2}$ shaded.

T R Y I T

Compare and Order Fractions (A)

Compare Fractions

Choose the answer.

1. This rectangle shows $\frac{1}{5}$ shaded.

   Which rectangle shows more than $\frac{1}{5}$ shaded?

   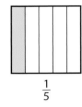
   $\frac{1}{5}$

   A.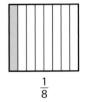
   $\frac{1}{8}$

   B.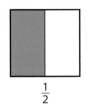
   $\frac{1}{2}$

   C.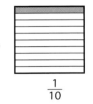
   $\frac{1}{10}$

   D.
   $\frac{1}{12}$

2. This rectangle shows $\frac{1}{6}$ shaded.

   Which rectangle shows more than $\frac{1}{6}$ shaded?

   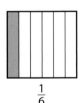
   $\frac{1}{6}$

   A.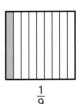
   $\frac{1}{9}$

   B.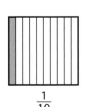
   $\frac{1}{10}$

   C.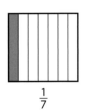
   $\frac{1}{7}$

   D.
   $\frac{1}{5}$

TRY IT

3. This rectangle shows $\frac{1}{4}$ shaded.

Which rectangle shows less than $\frac{1}{4}$ shaded?

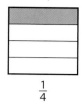
$\frac{1}{4}$

A.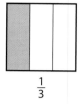
$\frac{1}{3}$

B.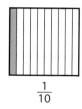
$\frac{1}{10}$

C.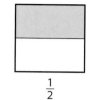
$\frac{1}{2}$

D.
$\frac{1}{1}$

4. This rectangle shows $\frac{1}{10}$ shaded.

Which rectangle shows less than $\frac{1}{10}$ shaded?

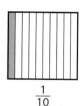
$\frac{1}{10}$

A.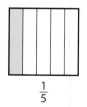
$\frac{1}{5}$

B.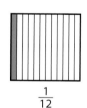
$\frac{1}{12}$

C.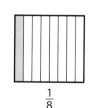
$\frac{1}{8}$

D.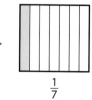
$\frac{1}{7}$

5. This rectangle shows $\frac{2}{5}$ shaded.

Which rectangle shows less than $\frac{2}{5}$ shaded?

$\frac{2}{5}$

A.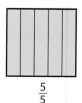
$\frac{5}{5}$

B.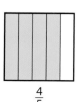
$\frac{4}{5}$

C.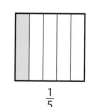
$\frac{1}{5}$

D.
$\frac{3}{5}$

FRACTIONS AND PROBABILITY

COMPARE AND ORDER FRACTIONS (A)

TRY IT

6. This rectangle shows $\frac{5}{9}$ shaded.

Which rectangle shows less than $\frac{5}{9}$ shaded?

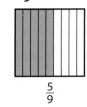
$\frac{5}{9}$

A.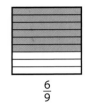
$\frac{6}{9}$

B.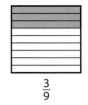
$\frac{3}{9}$

C.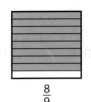
$\frac{8}{9}$

D.
$\frac{7}{9}$

7. Look at the number line showing $\frac{6}{8}, \frac{1}{8}, \frac{7}{8}$, and $\frac{3}{8}$.

Which comparison is correct?

A. $\frac{1}{8} < \frac{3}{8}$ B. $\frac{6}{8} < \frac{1}{8}$ C. $\frac{6}{8} < \frac{3}{8}$ D. $\frac{7}{8} < \frac{3}{8}$

8. Look at the number line showing $\frac{5}{6}, \frac{1}{6}, \frac{4}{6}$, and $\frac{3}{6}$.

Which comparison is correct?

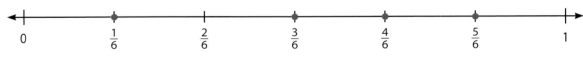

A. $\frac{5}{6} < \frac{1}{6}$ B. $\frac{3}{6} < \frac{4}{6}$ C. $\frac{5}{6} < \frac{3}{6}$ D. $\frac{4}{6} < \frac{1}{6}$

9. Look at the number line showing $\frac{4}{10}, \frac{9}{10}, \frac{2}{10}$, and $\frac{7}{10}$.

Which comparison is correct?

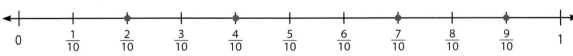

A. $\frac{2}{10} > \frac{7}{10}$ B. $\frac{7}{10} > \frac{9}{10}$ C. $\frac{9}{10} > \frac{2}{10}$ D. $\frac{4}{10} > \frac{7}{10}$

T R Y   I T

Compare and Order Fractions (B)

Use Number Lines to Compare Fractions

Worked Examples

You can use number lines to compare fractions.

PROBLEM Compare the fractions. Use <, >, or =.

$\frac{7}{12} \; \underline{?} \; \frac{11}{12}$

SOLUTION

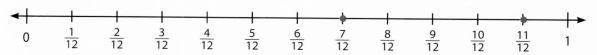

0    $\frac{1}{12}$ $\frac{2}{12}$ $\frac{3}{12}$ $\frac{4}{12}$ $\frac{5}{12}$ $\frac{6}{12}$ $\frac{7}{12}$ $\frac{8}{12}$ $\frac{9}{12}$ $\frac{10}{12}$ $\frac{11}{12}$ 1

Since both fractions are twelfths (they both have 12 in the denominator), you know that 7 twelfths is less than 11 twelfths. You can also locate $\frac{7}{12}$ and $\frac{11}{12}$ on the twelfths number line. The numbers on the number line get greater as you move to the right. The fraction $\frac{11}{12}$ is to the right of $\frac{7}{12}$. So $\frac{7}{12}$ is less than $\frac{11}{12}$.

ANSWER $\frac{7}{12} < \frac{11}{12}$

Compare the fractions. Use <, >, or =.

1. $\frac{1}{3} \; \underline{?} \; \frac{2}{3}$

2. $\frac{6}{8} \; \underline{?} \; \frac{3}{8}$

3. $\frac{4}{5} \; \underline{?} \; \frac{1}{5}$

4. $\frac{1}{4} \; \underline{?} \; \frac{2}{4}$

5. $\frac{3}{6} \; \underline{?} \; \frac{2}{6}$

6. $\frac{9}{10} \; \underline{?} \; \frac{5}{10}$

7. $\frac{4}{11} \; \underline{?} \; \frac{8}{11}$

8. $\frac{8}{12} \; \underline{?} \; \frac{2}{12}$

LEARN

Worked Examples

You can use number lines to order fractions.

PROBLEM Order the fractions from least to greatest.

$\frac{3}{4}, \frac{2}{4}$

SOLUTION

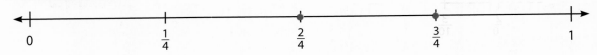

Since both fractions are fourths (they both have 4 in the denominator), you know that 2 fourths is less than 3 fourths. On the number line you can see that $\frac{2}{4}$ is to the left of $\frac{3}{4}$, so $\frac{2}{4}$ is less than $\frac{3}{4}$.

ANSWER $\frac{2}{4}, \frac{3}{4}$

Order the fractions from least to greatest.

9. $\frac{4}{6}, \frac{5}{6}$

10. $\frac{11}{12}, \frac{10}{12}$

11. $\frac{6}{10}, \frac{5}{10}, \frac{7}{10}$

12. $\frac{3}{3}, \frac{1}{3}, \frac{2}{3}$

13. $\frac{5}{8}, \frac{4}{8}, \frac{3}{8}$

14. $\frac{2}{12}, \frac{5}{12}, \frac{7}{12}$

L E A R N

Use the number lines showing $\frac{1}{3}$, $\frac{1}{4}$, $\frac{1}{6}$, and $\frac{1}{10}$ to solve Problems 15–19.

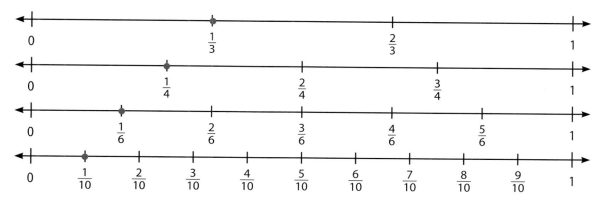

Compare the fractions. Use $<$, $>$, or $=$.

15. $\frac{1}{3}$ ___?___ $\frac{1}{6}$

16. $\frac{1}{10}$ ___?___ $\frac{1}{4}$

17. $\frac{1}{6}$ ___?___ $\frac{2}{6}$

Order the fractions from least to greatest.

18. $\frac{1}{6}$, $\frac{1}{10}$, $\frac{1}{4}$

19. $\frac{1}{3}$, $\frac{1}{4}$, $\frac{1}{6}$

LEARN

Compare and Order Fractions (B)

Compare and Order with Models

Read the problem and follow the directions.

1. Look at the shaded area of each rectangle.
   Write these fractions in order from least to greatest.

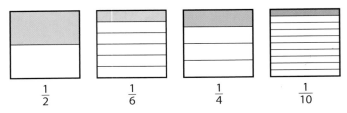

$\frac{1}{2}$ $\frac{1}{6}$ $\frac{1}{4}$ $\frac{1}{10}$

Choose the answer.

2. Look at the number line showing $\frac{4}{11}$, $\frac{9}{11}$, $\frac{1}{11}$, and $\frac{6}{11}$.
   Which comparison is correct?

A. $\frac{1}{11} > \frac{9}{11}$ B. $\frac{9}{11} > \frac{6}{11}$ C. $\frac{6}{11} < \frac{4}{11}$ D. $\frac{4}{11} < \frac{1}{11}$

3. Look at the number lines showing $\frac{1}{6}$, $\frac{1}{4}$, $\frac{1}{3}$, and $\frac{1}{10}$.
   Which comparison is correct?

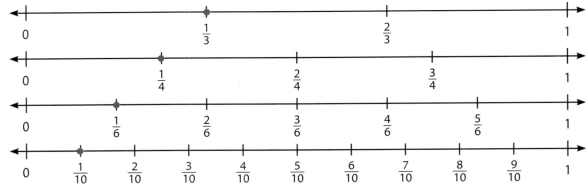

A. $\frac{1}{3} > \frac{1}{6}$ B. $\frac{1}{4} < \frac{1}{6}$ C. $\frac{1}{3} < \frac{1}{10}$ D. $\frac{1}{10} > \frac{1}{4}$

TRY IT

4. Look at the shaded area of each rectangle.
Which option shows these fractions in order from least to greatest?

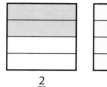

$\frac{2}{4}$ $\qquad$ $\frac{4}{4}$ $\qquad$ $\frac{1}{4}$ $\qquad$ $\frac{3}{4}$

A. $\frac{4}{4}, \frac{3}{4}, \frac{2}{4}, \frac{1}{4}$ $\qquad$ B. $\frac{3}{4}, \frac{2}{4}, \frac{4}{4}, \frac{1}{4}$

C. $\frac{2}{4}, \frac{3}{4}, \frac{1}{4}, \frac{4}{4}$ $\qquad$ D. $\frac{1}{4}, \frac{2}{4}, \frac{3}{4}, \frac{4}{4}$

5. This rectangle shows $\frac{1}{4}$ shaded. Which rectangle shows more than $\frac{1}{4}$ shaded?

$\frac{1}{4}$

A. $\qquad$ B. $\qquad$ C. $\qquad$ D.

$\frac{1}{3}$ $\qquad$ $\frac{1}{11}$ $\qquad$ $\frac{1}{8}$ $\qquad$ $\frac{1}{10}$

6. This rectangle shows $\frac{1}{6}$ shaded. Which rectangle shows less than $\frac{1}{6}$ shaded?

$\frac{1}{6}$

A. 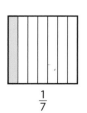 $\qquad$ B. 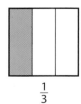 $\qquad$ C. 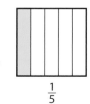 $\qquad$ D.

$\frac{1}{7}$ $\qquad$ $\frac{1}{3}$ $\qquad$ $\frac{1}{5}$ $\qquad$ $\frac{1}{2}$

T R Y   I T

7. Look at the number lines showing $\frac{1}{8}$, $\frac{1}{2}$, $\frac{1}{12}$, and $\frac{1}{6}$.
Which comparison is correct?

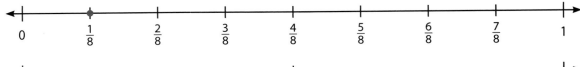

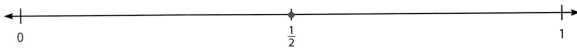

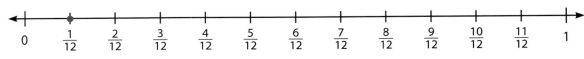

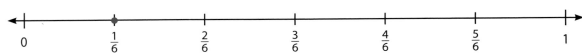

A. $\frac{1}{8} > \frac{1}{6}$ B. $\frac{1}{6} > \frac{1}{2}$ C. $\frac{1}{2} > \frac{1}{12}$ D. $\frac{1}{12} > \frac{1}{6}$

8. Look at the number lines showing $\frac{1}{3}$, $\frac{1}{4}$, $\frac{1}{11}$, and $\frac{1}{6}$.
Which comparison is correct?

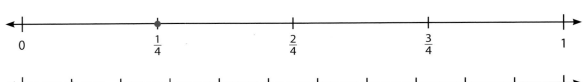

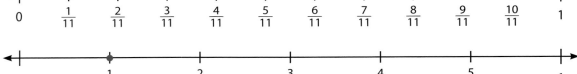

A. $\frac{1}{3} > \frac{1}{11}$ B. $\frac{1}{11} > \frac{1}{6}$ C. $\frac{1}{6} > \frac{1}{4}$ D. $\frac{1}{4} > \frac{1}{3}$

T R Y I T

9. Look at the number lines showing $\frac{1}{3}$, $\frac{1}{8}$, $\frac{1}{5}$, and $\frac{1}{2}$.
Which comparison is correct?

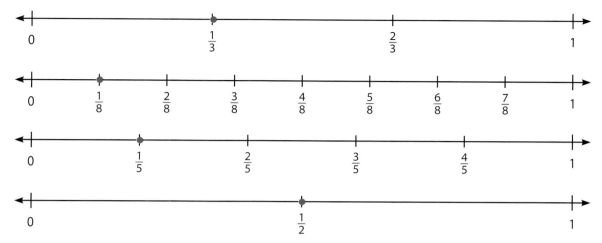

A. $\frac{1}{3} < \frac{1}{5}$ B. $\frac{1}{5} < \frac{1}{8}$ C. $\frac{1}{8} < \frac{1}{2}$ D. $\frac{1}{2} < \frac{1}{5}$

10. Look at the number line showing $\frac{7}{9}$, $\frac{1}{9}$, $\frac{4}{9}$, and $\frac{8}{9}$.
Which comparison is correct?

A. $\frac{8}{9} < \frac{1}{9}$ B. $\frac{7}{9} < \frac{4}{9}$ C. $\frac{4}{9} < \frac{8}{9}$ D. $\frac{7}{9} < \frac{1}{9}$

11. Look at the shaded area of each rectangle.
Which option shows these fractions arranged from least to greatest?

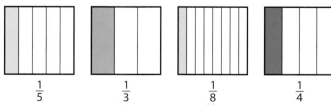

$\frac{1}{5}$ $\frac{1}{3}$ $\frac{1}{8}$ $\frac{1}{4}$

A. $\frac{1}{3}, \frac{1}{4}, \frac{1}{5}, \frac{1}{8}$ B. $\frac{1}{4}, \frac{1}{5}, \frac{1}{8}, \frac{1}{3}$

C. $\frac{1}{5}, \frac{1}{8}, \frac{1}{3}, \frac{1}{4}$ D. $\frac{1}{8}, \frac{1}{5}, \frac{1}{4}, \frac{1}{3}$

T R Y   I T

12. Look at the shaded area of each rectangle.
Which option shows these fractions arranged from greatest to least?

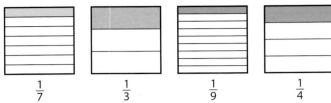

$\frac{1}{7}$ $\frac{1}{3}$ $\frac{1}{9}$ $\frac{1}{4}$

A. $\frac{1}{9}, \frac{1}{7}, \frac{1}{3}, \frac{1}{4}$ B. $\frac{1}{3}, \frac{1}{4}, \frac{1}{9}, \frac{1}{7}$

C. $\frac{1}{9}, \frac{1}{4}, \frac{1}{3}, \frac{1}{7}$ D. $\frac{1}{3}, \frac{1}{4}, \frac{1}{7}, \frac{1}{9}$

13. Look at the shaded area of each rectangle.
Which option shows these fractions arranged from least to greatest?

$\frac{12}{12}$ $\frac{1}{12}$ $\frac{8}{12}$ $\frac{4}{12}$

A. $\frac{12}{12}, \frac{8}{12}, \frac{4}{12}, \frac{1}{12}$ B. $\frac{12}{12}, \frac{1}{12}, \frac{8}{12}, \frac{4}{12}$

C. $\frac{1}{12}, \frac{4}{12}, \frac{8}{12}, \frac{12}{12}$ D. $\frac{4}{12}, \frac{1}{12}, \frac{8}{12}, \frac{12}{12}$

TRY IT

Model Fraction Story Problems

Use Drawings for Fraction Stories

Worked Examples

You can use drawings to solve fraction story problems.

PROBLEM Brandon jogs $\frac{3}{6}$ mile and then walks $\frac{4}{6}$ mile. How far has Brandon traveled?

SOLUTION

1 Model the problem. Jump to $\frac{3}{6}$ on the number line. Then jump $\frac{4}{6}$ more to $\frac{7}{6}$.

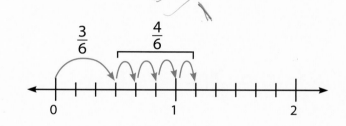

2 Write the addition number sentence for the problem: $\frac{3}{6} + \frac{4}{6} = \frac{7}{6}$. The fraction $\frac{7}{6}$ is greater than 1, so write it as a mixed number, $1\frac{1}{6}$.

ANSWER Brandon has traveled $1\frac{1}{6}$ miles.

Draw a sketch or number line to model and solve the problem.

1. Anne is watching a grasshopper in the garden. It jumps $\frac{3}{6}$ yard the first jump and $\frac{2}{6}$ yard the second jump. How far has it jumped altogether?

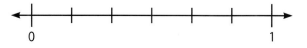

L E A R N

2. Favio's backyard fence has 7 equal sections. He paints $\frac{2}{7}$ of the fence on Saturday. On Sunday he paints $\frac{3}{7}$ of the fence.

How much of the fence has Favio painted so far?

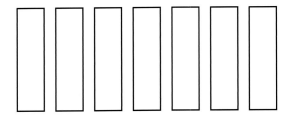

3. Zeke had a long rope. He cut the rope into two pieces. One piece is $2\frac{3}{5}$ feet long and the other piece is $1\frac{1}{5}$ feet long.

How long was the rope Zeke started with?

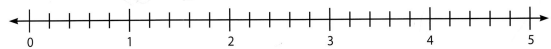

4. The blue hiking trail is $\frac{5}{8}$ mile long. Carolyn is $\frac{3}{8}$ mile from the end of the trail.

How much has Carolyn hiked?

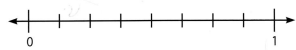

5. Mr. Carver has a board $2\frac{3}{4}$ yards long. He cuts off a piece $\frac{1}{4}$ yard long.

How long is the board now?

Model Fraction Story Problems

Sketch to Solve Fraction Problems

Worked Examples

You can draw a sketch to solve fraction problems.

PROBLEM Mr. Jordan cuts a pan of lasagna into 12 equal-sized pieces. Mike eats $\frac{3}{12}$ of the lasagna and Tina eats $\frac{2}{12}$ of the lasagna. What fraction of the lasagna have Mike and Tina eaten in all?

SOLUTION

1 Draw a rectangle to represent the lasagna. Draw lines to show the lasagna cut into 12 equal-sized pieces.

2 Shade the sketch to show how much of the lasagna Mike eats $\left(\frac{3}{12}, \text{ or 3 pieces}\right)$ and how much Tina eats $\left(\frac{2}{12}, \text{ or 2 pieces}\right)$. Count how many parts are shaded and write the amount as a fraction of the whole $\left(\frac{5}{12}\right)$.

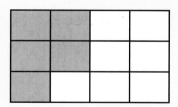

$$\frac{3}{12} + \frac{2}{12} = \frac{5}{12}$$

3 Write the number sentence under the sketch.

ANSWER Mike and Tina have eaten $\frac{5}{12}$ of the lasagna.

L E A R N

Draw a sketch or number line to model and solve the problem.

1. Aaron is jogging along a trail that goes around the lake.

   The trail is $2\frac{4}{5}$ miles. So far, Aaron has jogged $1\frac{3}{5}$ miles.

   How much farther does Aaron have left to jog?

   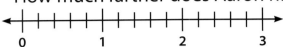

2. Deidre buys $2\frac{5}{6}$ yards of ribbon.

   She uses $\frac{4}{6}$ yard to decorate a gift.

   How much ribbon does Deidre have left?

3. Mrs. Kish bakes 2 pizzas. She cuts each pizza into 8 equal slices.

   Lee and his friends eat $\frac{7}{8}$ of a pizza and Mrs. Kish eats $\frac{2}{8}$ of a pizza.

   How much of the pizzas do they eat altogether?

   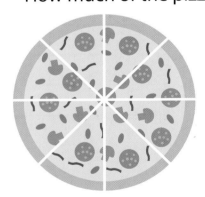 

LEARN

Model Fraction Story Problems

Draw Fraction Story Problems

Use the model to solve the problem.

1. Mr. Parker bakes an apple pie. He gives $\frac{5}{12}$ of the pie to his neighbor and $\frac{1}{12}$ of the pie to Mark.

   How much of the pie does Mr. Parker give away?

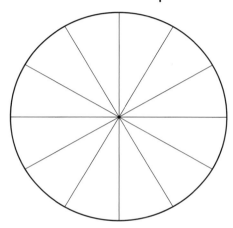

2. The road crew is fixing a $2\frac{5}{8}$-mile length of road. The first day, the workers fixed $1\frac{1}{8}$ miles of the road.

   How much do the workers have left to fix?

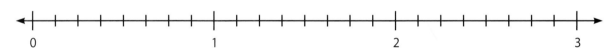

0   1   2   3

T R Y   I T

Choose the answer.

3. Tom planted seeds in $\frac{1}{5}$ of the flower bed. He then planted seeds in $\frac{3}{5}$ of the flower bed.

   How much of the flower bed had seeds?

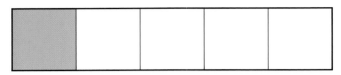

   A. $\frac{5}{5}$ B. $\frac{4}{5}$ C. $\frac{1}{5}$ D. $\frac{4}{10}$

4. The girls ate $3\frac{2}{4}$ submarine sandwiches. The boys ate $3\frac{1}{4}$ submarine sandwiches.

   How many submarine sandwiches did the children eat altogether?

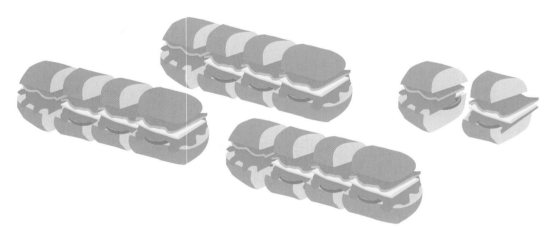

   A. $6\frac{3}{4}$ B. $6\frac{1}{4}$ C. $5\frac{3}{4}$ D. $4\frac{3}{6}$

TRY IT

5. Mike found $\frac{7}{8}$ of a pizza in the refrigerator. He ate $\frac{3}{8}$ of the pizza.

How much of the pizza was left?

A. $\frac{1}{8}$ B. $\frac{2}{8}$ C. $\frac{3}{8}$ D. $\frac{4}{8}$

6. Before lunch the restaurant had $4\frac{5}{6}$ pies. They sold $2\frac{3}{6}$ pies at lunch.

How many pies did the restaurant have left after lunch?

A. $2\frac{2}{6}$ B. $2\frac{5}{6}$ C. $3\frac{2}{6}$ D. $8\frac{8}{6}$

7. Hector used $3\frac{1}{3}$ cups white flour in his pizza dough. He also used $1\frac{1}{3}$ cups wheat flour.

How much flour did Hector use in his pizza dough altogether?

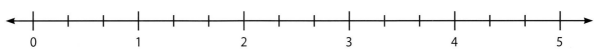

A. $2\frac{2}{3}$ cups B. $3\frac{2}{3}$ cups C. $4\frac{1}{3}$ cups D. $4\frac{2}{3}$ cups

TRY IT

Add and Subtract Like Fractions

Solve Fraction Story Problems

You can simplify sums and differences of fractions when solving story problems.

PROBLEM Roger cut a pizza into sixths. Roger ate $\frac{2}{6}$ of the pizza, Jenny ate $\frac{1}{6}$ of the pizza, and Tony ate $\frac{1}{6}$ of the pizza. How much of the pizza is left?

SOLUTION

1 Write a number sentence to find how much pizza the three friends ate altogether.

$$\frac{2}{6} + \frac{1}{6} + \frac{1}{6} = \frac{4}{6}$$

2 Write another number sentence to find how much pizza is left.

$$\frac{6}{6} - \frac{4}{6} = \frac{2}{6}$$

3 Simplify.

$$\frac{2}{6} = \frac{1}{3}$$

ANSWER There is $\frac{1}{3}$ of the pizza left.

Solve. Write the answer in simplest form. Use fraction strips to simplify the fractions.

1. Erin walked $\frac{3}{10}$ mile to the post office, and then she walked $\frac{5}{10}$ mile to the library.

   How far did Erin walk altogether?

LEARN

2. Harper has a board that is $\frac{7}{8}$ feet long.
He cuts off a piece that is $\frac{5}{8}$ feet long.

How long is the board now?

3. Elias used $\frac{3}{4}$ cup of brown sugar and $\frac{3}{4}$ cup of white sugar to make trail bars.

How much total sugar did Elias use?

LEARN

Add and Subtract Like Fractions

Solve and Simplify

Add or subtract. Write the answer in simplest form. Use fraction strips to simplify the fractions.

1. $\frac{7}{10} + \frac{2}{10}$

2. $\frac{5}{6} - \frac{1}{6}$

3. $1\frac{3}{4} + 1\frac{1}{4}$

4. $2\frac{5}{8} + 1\frac{5}{8}$

5. Mia and Patty are knitting scarves. So far, Mia has knit $\frac{7}{12}$ yard and Patty has knit $\frac{5}{12}$ yard.
   How much more has Mia knit than Patty?

6. Rita walked $\frac{4}{5}$ mile to her friend's house, and then she walked $\frac{4}{5}$ mile back to her house.
   How far did Rita walk altogether?

Choose the answer. Be sure the answer is in simplest form.

7. $\frac{3}{7} + \frac{2}{7} = ?$

   A. $\frac{1}{7}$ B. $\frac{4}{7}$ C. $\frac{5}{7}$ D. $\frac{5}{14}$

8. $\frac{1}{4} + \frac{1}{4} = ?$

   A. $\frac{1}{2}$ B. $\frac{1}{4}$ C. $\frac{3}{4}$ D. $\frac{2}{8}$

9. $\frac{11}{12} - \frac{9}{12} = ?$

   A. $\frac{2}{0}$ B. $\frac{1}{6}$ C. $\frac{1}{12}$ D. $\frac{20}{12}$

TRY IT

10. $1\frac{5}{7} + 2\frac{1}{7} = ?$

A. $3\frac{6}{14}$ B. $3\frac{5}{7}$ C. $3\frac{6}{7}$ D. $4\frac{1}{7}$

11. $2\frac{2}{3} - 1\frac{1}{3} = ?$

A. $1\frac{1}{0}$ B. $1\frac{1}{3}$ C. $2\frac{1}{3}$ D. 4

12. $2\frac{1}{8} + 4\frac{1}{8} = ?$

A. $6\frac{2}{16}$ B. $3\frac{1}{8}$ C. $6\frac{3}{8}$ D. $6\frac{1}{4}$

13. $4\frac{5}{9} - 2\frac{2}{9} = ?$

A. $1\frac{2}{3}$ B. 2 C. $2\frac{1}{3}$ D. $2\frac{2}{3}$

14. Suzanna bought $\frac{1}{6}$ yard of brown fabric and $\frac{1}{6}$ yard of blue fabric. How much fabric did Suzanna buy?

A. $\frac{2}{12}$ yard   B. $\frac{3}{6}$ yard   C. $\frac{1}{3}$ yard   D. $\frac{1}{4}$ yard

15. Mark walked $\frac{3}{8}$ mile in the morning and $\frac{1}{8}$ mile during lunch. How much did Mark walk in total?

A. $\frac{2}{0}$ mile   B. $\frac{1}{2}$ mile   C. $\frac{4}{16}$ mile   D. $\frac{3}{8}$ mile

16. Desiree needed $2\frac{2}{3}$ yards of material to make bedsheets and $1\frac{2}{3}$ yards to make the pillowcase. How much material did Desiree need altogether?

A. $3\frac{1}{3}$ yards   B. $3\frac{2}{3}$ yards   C. $4\frac{1}{3}$ yards   D. $4\frac{2}{3}$ yards

TRY IT

Fractions and Decimals (A)

Different Ways to Show the Same Thing

Write the fraction as a decimal.

1. $\frac{4}{10}$

2. $\frac{9}{100}$

3. $\frac{3}{1,000}$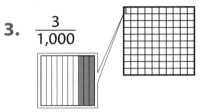

Write the decimal as a fraction.

4. 0.2

5. 0.7

6. 0.05

Read the problem and follow the directions.

7. Write 36 hundredths as a fraction and a decimal.

8. Julia drank $\frac{7}{10}$ cup of juice and 0.7 cup of water.
    Did Julia drink more water, more juice, or the same
    amounts of water and juice? Explain your answer.

Choose the answer.

9. Mike shaded $\frac{7}{10}$ of this rectangle.
    Which decimal equals $\frac{7}{10}$?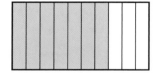

    A. 0.07   B. 0.7   C. 7.0   D. 7.10

10. Petros shaded $\frac{5}{10}$ of this rectangle.
    Which decimal equals $\frac{5}{10}$?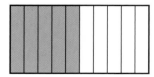

    A. 0.5   B. 0.51   C. 5.0   D. 5.10

T R Y   I T

11. Remi shaded 0.6 of this rectangle. Which fraction equals 0.6?

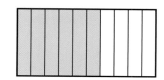

    A. $\frac{1}{6}$ B. $\frac{6}{10}$ C. $\frac{6}{1}$ D. $\frac{60}{1}$

12. Which decimal is equal to $\frac{1}{10}$?

    A. 0.01   B. 0.10   C. 1.0   D. 1.1

13. Which decimal is equal to $\frac{5}{10}$?

    A. 0.5   B. 0.51   C. 5.0   D. 5.1

14. Which fraction is equal to 0.6?

    A. $\frac{1}{6}$ B. $\frac{0}{6}$ C. $\frac{6}{10}$ D. $\frac{6}{100}$

15. Which fraction is equal to 0.3?

    A. $\frac{3}{100}$ B. $\frac{1}{30}$ C. $\frac{3}{10}$ D. $\frac{1}{3}$

16. Which fraction is equal to 0.75?

    A. $\frac{75}{1}$ B. $\frac{75}{10}$ C. $\frac{1}{75}$ D. $\frac{75}{100}$

17. Which fraction is equal to 0.5? Express your answer in simplest form.

    A. $\frac{1}{2}$ B. $\frac{5}{100}$ C. $\frac{10}{5}$ D. $\frac{5}{1,000}$

TRY IT

Fractions and Decimals (B)

Same Amount in Fraction and Decimal

Write the number as a fraction.

1. 0.7

2. 0.25

3. 0.02

Write the number as a decimal.

4. $\frac{2}{5}$

5. $\frac{1}{2}$

6. $\frac{3}{4}$

Write the number as a decimal in tenths and hundredths.
Write the equivalent fractions for those decimals.

7. $\frac{1}{2}$

8. $\frac{1}{5}$

9. $\frac{4}{5}$

Read the problem and follow the directions.

10. Draw a number line that shows $\frac{2}{4}$.

    Write a fraction and a decimal that equal $\frac{2}{4}$.

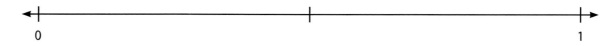

11. Write 3 tenths as a fraction and as a decimal. Use a number line to show why they represent the same quantity.

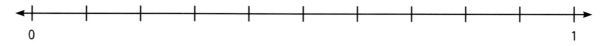

12. Johnny and Winnie are weaving placemats. Johnny has completed 0.4 of his placemat and Winnie has completed $\frac{2}{5}$ of her placemat. Who has the least amount left to weave? Explain.

TRY IT

Choose the answer.

13. Which decimal is equal to $\frac{7}{10}$?

    A. 0.07   B. 0.071   C. 0.7   D. 0.71

14. Which decimal is equal to $\frac{3}{5}$?

    A. 0.6   B. 6.0   C. 0.35   D. 3.5

15. Which fraction is equal to 0.25?

    A. $\frac{25}{10}$ B. $\frac{1}{25}$ C. $\frac{10}{25}$ D. $\frac{25}{100}$

16. Which fraction is equal to 0.6?
    Express your answer in simplest form.

    A. $\frac{6}{1}$ B. $\frac{5}{3}$ C. $\frac{3}{5}$ D. $\frac{1}{6}$

17. Which decimal is equal to $\frac{4}{5}$?

    A. 4.0, because this is the same as $\frac{4}{10}$, which simplifies to $\frac{4}{5}$

    B. 8.0, because this is the same as $\frac{8}{10}$, which simplifies to $\frac{4}{5}$

    C. 0.8, because this is the same as $\frac{8}{10}$, which simplifies to $\frac{4}{5}$

    D. 0.4, because this is the same as $\frac{4}{10}$, which simplifies to $\frac{4}{5}$

TRY IT

Identify, Record, and Display Outcomes

Find the Outcome

Memory Jogger

Here are some different ways to show the outcome of a probability experiment:

TALLY CHART

Experiment: Squares from a Bag	
Color of squares	**Tally**
Green	||||
Red	||||| ||
Blue	||||
Yellow	|||

LINE PLOT

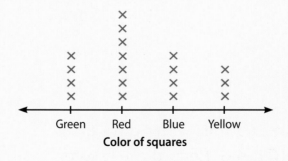

Experiment: Squares from a Bag

HORIZONTAL BAR GRAPH

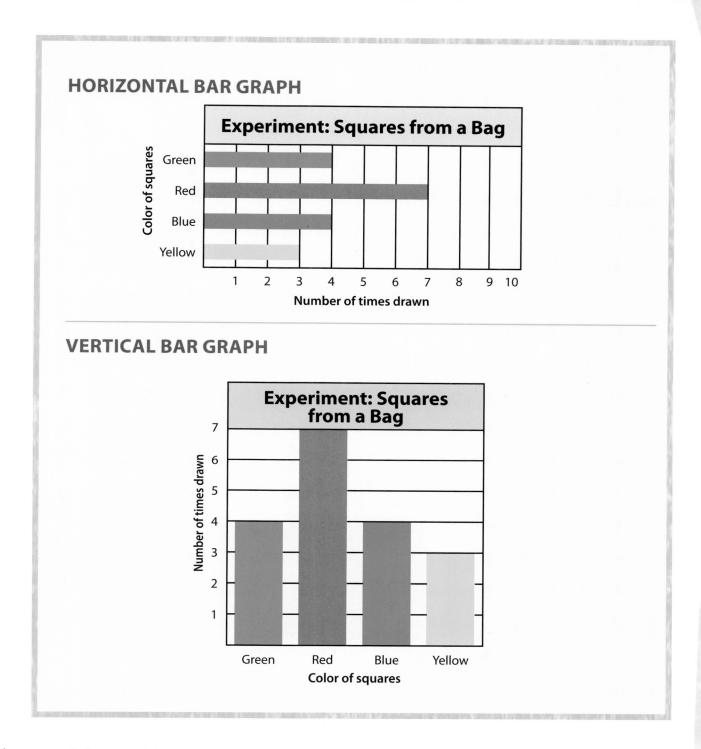

Experiment: Squares from a Bag

Color of squares — Green, Red, Blue, Yellow

Number of times drawn

VERTICAL BAR GRAPH

Experiment: Squares from a Bag

Number of times drawn

Color of squares — Green, Red, Blue, Yellow

Read the problem and follow the directions.

1. Toss a coin 10 times. Record the results (heads or tails) on a tally chart.

Coin Toss Results	
Outcomes	**Tally**
Heads	
Tails	

T R Y   I T

Choose the answer.

2. Which outcome is **not** possible if the spinner is spun once?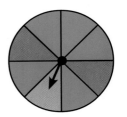
   - A. green
   - B. blue
   - C. orange
   - D. red

3. Kiera spun a spinner 12 times. She got these numbers on her spins: 1, 1, 2, 3, 1, 1, 2, 2, 1, 3, 4, 1.

   Which line plot shows these results?

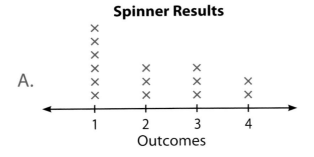

A.

Spinner Results

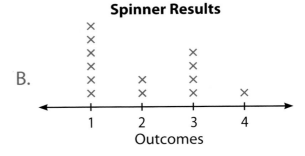

B.

Spinner Results

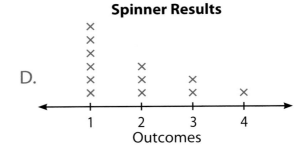

C.

Spinner Results

D.

Spinner Results

4. Josie reached into a bag with 6 red marbles, 8 green marbles, and 2 blue marbles. She pulled out a marble.

   Which color marble could Josie pull out?
   - A. green, orange, or blue
   - B. yellow, blue, or red
   - C. blue, green, or red
   - D. black, red, or green

T R Y I T

5. Niki spun a spinner 20 times and recorded the results on this tally chart.

Which bar graph correctly shows these results?

Spinner Results	
Color	**Tally**
Yellow	~~IIII~~ IIII
Orange	~~IIII~~ II
Green	IIII

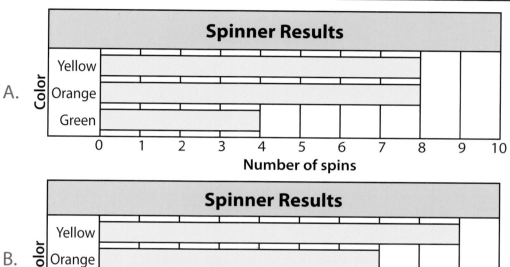

A.

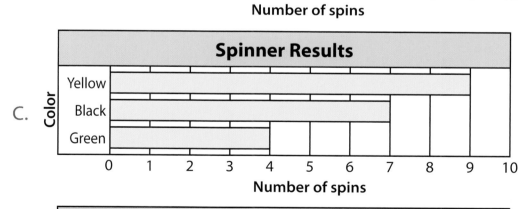

B.

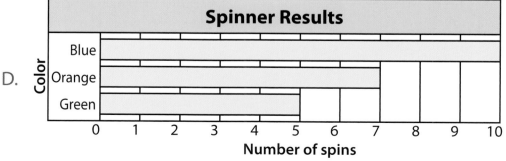

C.

D.

TRY IT

6. Which outcome is **not** possible if one ball is taken out of this jar?

A. purple ball   B. green ball

C. brown ball   D. white ball

7. Geoff rolled a number cube 15 times. He rolled these numbers:
3, 6, 4, 2, 3, 1, 5, 6, 6, 4, 2, 5, 3, 2, 4. Which tally chart shows these results?

A.

Number Cube Results	
Number	Tally
1	|
2	|||
3	|||
4	|||
5	||
6	|||

B.

Number Cube Results	
Number	Tally
1	|
2	||
3	|||
4	|||
5	|||
6	|||

C.

Number Cube Results	
Number	Tally
1	|||
2	|||
3	|||
4	|||
5	||
6	|||

D.

Number Cube Results	
Number	Tally
1	|
2	|
3	|||
4	||
5	||
6	|||

TRY IT

Use Data to Make Predictions

What Will Happen Next?

Worked Examples

You can use data to make predictions for future events.

PROBLEM At a carnival, a giant wheel is spun to see which prize you win. The bar graph shows the prizes given out each day for four days. Use the data to predict which prize will be given out the most times on Sunday.

SOLUTION Far more yo-yos were given out than any other prize. And the yo-yo section of the spinner is much larger than any other section. So yo-yos will probably be given out the most times on Sunday.

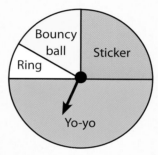

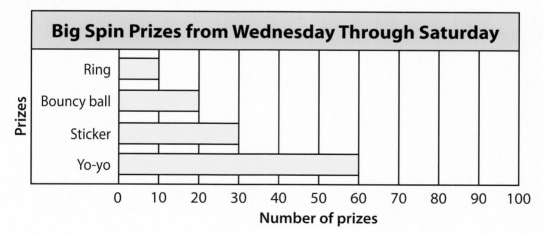

Big Spin Prizes from Wednesday Through Saturday

Prizes (vertical axis): Ring, Bouncy ball, Sticker, Yo-yo

Number of prizes (horizontal axis): 0 10 20 30 40 50 60 70 80 90 100

ANSWER Yo-yos will probably be given out the most times on Sunday.

L E A R N

Use the data to predict future events.

1. Eddie tosses a number cube with the numbers 1, 2, and 3 on it. The line plot shows the results of his tosses. If he tosses the cube 30 more times, predict which number is likely to show the most times.

Number Cube Rolls

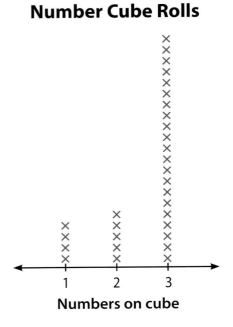

2. Sydney has a bag of number tiles. She draws a tile from the bag 23 times, replacing it each time. The tally chart shows the results. If Sydney draws and replaces tiles 23 more times, predict which number is most likely to be drawn the most times.

Number Tiles Drawn	
Number	**Tally**
1	||
2	||
3	|||
4														
5	|
6	||

LEARN

3. Brady spins the spinner 36 times. He records the outcomes in the line plot. Predict the color that would most likely be spun the most if Brady spins the spinner 36 more times.

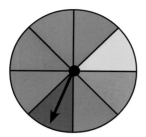

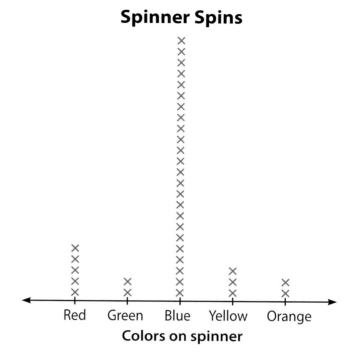

Spinner Spins

L E A R N

Use Data to Make Predictions

Make a Prediction

Use the data to predict future events.

1. Rita spun a spinner 17 times and recorded the outcomes in a bar graph. If she spins the spinner 17 more times, predict the color that the spinner would most likely land on most often.

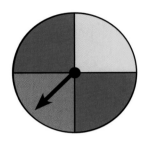

Spinner Results

Color	Number of spins
Green	(bar to 11)
Yellow	(bar to 1)
Red	(bar to 4)

Number of spins: 0 1 2 3 4 5 6 7 8 9 10 11 12 13 14 15 16 17

2. Charlie spun a spinner 32 times and recorded the outcomes in a tally chart. If he spins the spinner 32 more times, which color would the spinner be least likely to land on?

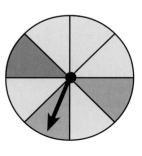

Spinner Results	
Color	**Tally**
Red	卌 卌 卌 卌 卌 |||
Yellow	||||

Choose the answer.

3. If Tina spins this spinner 30 times, which color will most likely be landed on the most?

A. pink   B. purple

C. red   D. orange

4. Lauren spun the spinner 32 times and recorded the numbers that the spinner landed on.

   If Lauren spins the spinner another 24 times, which number will most likely be landed on the most?

   A. 1

   B. 2

   C. 3

   D. 4

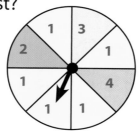

Spinner Results

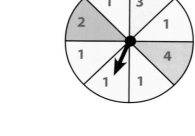

Numbers on spinner

5. Paulina spun the spinner 24 times and recorded the letters that the spinner landed on.

   If Paulina spins the spinner another 24 times, which letter will most likely be landed on the most?

   A. W

   B. X

   C. Y

   D. Z

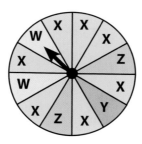

Spinner Results	
Letter	Tally
W	IIII
X	TTTT TTTT IIII
Y	II
Z	IIII

6. Kylie pulled a square from a bag 40 times, recorded the color of the square, and then put it back in the bag.

   If Kylie pulls out a square another 20 times, which square will most likely be chosen the most?

   A. yellow   B. green

   C. blue   D. red

Squares Drawn	
Color	Tally
Green	TTTT I
Red	TTTT TTTT TTTT TTTT
Blue	TTTT TTTT
Yellow	IIII

T R Y   I T

7. Lizzie spun the spinner 25 times. On this line plot, she recorded the numbers that the spinner landed on.

If Lizzie spins the spinner another 20 times, which number will most likely be landed on the most?

A. 4
B. 3
C. 2
D. 1

Spinner Results

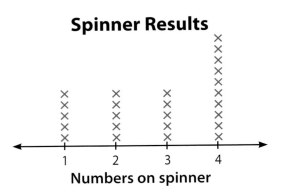

Numbers on spinner

8. Xavier had a number cube with the numbers 1, 1, 3, 2, 2, and 2. He rolled his number cube 12 times. On this line plot, he recorded the number of times he rolled each number.

If Xavier rolls his number cube another 24 times, which number will most likely be rolled the most?

A. 1
B. 2
C. 3

Number Rolled

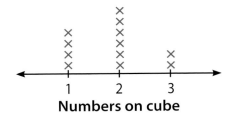

Numbers on cube

9. Hilary spun the spinner 18 times. On this line plot, she recorded the numbers that the spinner landed on.

If Hilary spins the spinner another 27 times, which number will most likely be landed on the most?

A. 1
B. 2
C. 3
D. 4

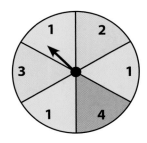

Spinner Results

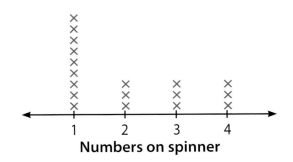

Numbers on spinner

TRY IT

Estimate and Measure Centimeters

Round to the Nearest Centimeter

You can use a ruler to measure objects to the nearest centimeter.

PROBLEM Measure the line to the nearest centimeter.

SOLUTION

1 Place the ruler below the line so the left end of the line exactly matches up with 0 on the ruler.

2 Look at the right end of the line to see which centimeter mark it's closest to. If it falls exactly in the middle between two centimeter marks, use the greater number. The line is just a little greater than the $6\frac{1}{2}$-centimeter mark. So the line is 7 centimeters long when measured to the nearest centimeter.

ANSWER 7 cm

L E A R N

Measure the line to the nearest centimeter.

1. ⊢—⊣

2. ⊢———⊣

3. ⊢————————⊣

4. ⊢———————————————⊣

5. ⊢————————————⊣

6. ⊢———⊣

7. ⊢——————————————⊣

LEARN

Estimate and Measure Centimeters

Centimeter Measures

Measure the object to the nearest centimeter.

1. What is the length of the feather to the nearest centimeter?

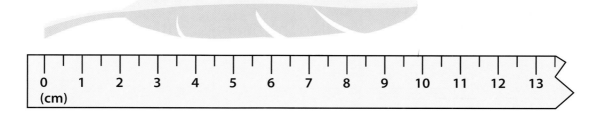

2. What is the length of the candle to the nearest centimeter, including the wick?

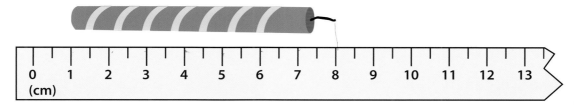

Read the problem and follow the directions.

3. Estimate the length of the fork. Then measure the length of the fork to the nearest centimeter.

4. Estimate the length of a table. Then measure the length of the table to the nearest centimeter.

TRY IT

Choose the answer.

5. What is the length of the toothpick to the nearest centimeter?

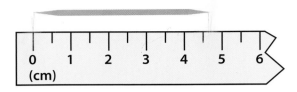

A. 1 cm   B. 5 cm   C. 2 cm   D. 8 cm

6. What is the length of the pencil to the nearest centimeter?

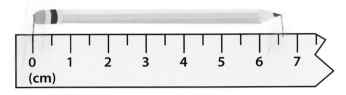

A. 3 cm   B. 5 cm   C. 7 cm   D. 9 cm

7. Estimate the width of the stamp.

A. about 2 cm
B. about 3 cm
C. about 4 cm
D. about 5 cm

8. Estimate the length of the crayon.

A. about 5 cm   B. about 10 cm
C. about 15 cm   D. about 20 cm

TRY IT

9. Estimate the height of the bamboo plant.

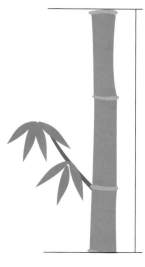

A. about 1 cm   B. about 6 cm

C. about 8 cm   D. about 7 cm

10. Estimate the height of the flower, including stem.

A. about 5 cm   B. about 10 cm

C. about 20 cm   D. about 25 cm

TRY IT

Estimate and Measure Inches (A)

Measure to the Nearest Quarter Inch

Worked Examples

You can use a ruler to measure objects to the nearest quarter inch.

PROBLEM   Measure the line to the nearest quarter inch.

SOLUTION

1 Place the ruler below the line so the left end of the line exactly matches up with 0 on the ruler.

2 Look at the right end of the line to see which quarter-inch mark it's closest to. If it falls exactly in the middle between two quarter-inch marks, round it to the greater mark. The line is exactly between the marks for $3\frac{1}{2}$ inches and $3\frac{3}{4}$ inches. So round to the greater quarter inch. The measure of the line rounded to the nearest quarter inch is $3\frac{3}{4}$ inches.

ANSWER $3\frac{3}{4}$ in.

LEARN

Measure the line to the nearest quarter inch.

1. ├─────────────────┤

2. ├──────────┤

3. ├──────────────────────────┤

4. ├──────┤

5. ├──┤

6. ├────────────┤

LEARN

Estimate and Measure Inches (A)

Find the Nearest Quarter Inch

Measure to the nearest quarter inch.

1.

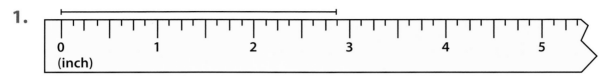

2.

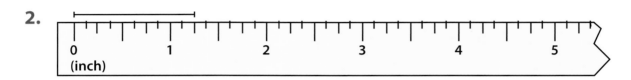

3.

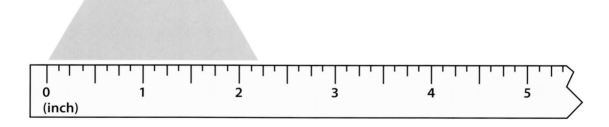

4.

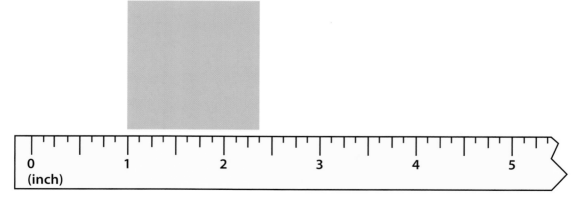

TRY IT

Read the problem and follow the directions.

5. Find three items in your home. Estimate the length of each object. Then measure each object to the nearest quarter inch. Record the name and measurement of each object in your notebook.

Use this ruler to solve Problems 6–12. Choose the answer.

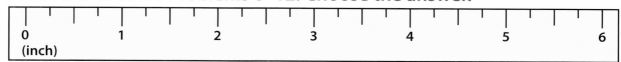

6. Estimate the length of the spoon.

   A. about 3 in.   B. about 5 in.

   C. about 10 in.   D. about 15 in.

7. Estimate the length of the spatula.

   A. about 5 in.   B. about 6 in.

   C. about 7 in.   D. about 8 in.

8. What is the length of the crayon?

   A. $3\frac{1}{2}$ in.   B. $3\frac{3}{4}$ in.   C. 4 in.   D. $4\frac{1}{4}$ in.

TRY IT

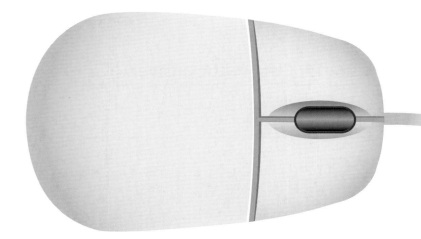

9. What is the length of the computer mouse?

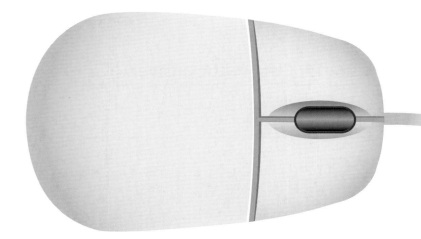

A. $2\frac{1}{2}$ in.   B. $2\frac{3}{4}$ in.   C. 3 in.   D. $3\frac{3}{4}$ in.

10. What is the length of the ice pop?

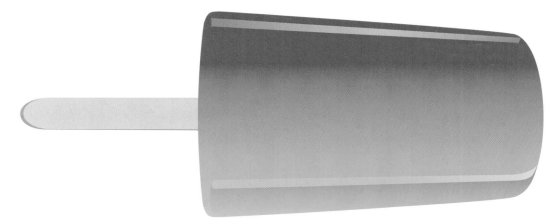

A. $5\frac{1}{4}$ in.   B. $5\frac{1}{2}$ in.   C. $5\frac{3}{4}$ in.   D. $6\frac{1}{2}$ in.

TRY IT

11. What is the length of the envelope?

A. $3\frac{2}{4}$ in.   B. $3\frac{3}{4}$ in.   C. 4 in.   D. $4\frac{1}{4}$ in.

12. Estimate the length of the key.
Then measure the length of the key to the nearest quarter inch.

T R Y   I T

Estimate and Measure Inches (B)

Measure to a Quarter Inch

Estimate the measurement. Use a ruler to find the actual measurement to the nearest quarter inch.

1. Length of your favorite book
   Estimate?
   Actual?

2. Length of your foot
   Estimate?
   Actual?

3. Width of a plate
   Estimate?
   Actual?

4. Length of a desk
   Estimate?
   Actual?

Choose the answer.

5. What is the length of the worm?

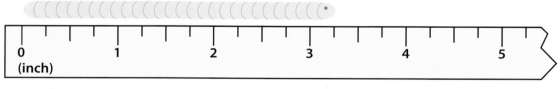

A. $2\frac{1}{4}$ in.   B. 3 in.   C. $3\frac{1}{4}$ in.   D. 4 in.

6. What is the length of the toy train?

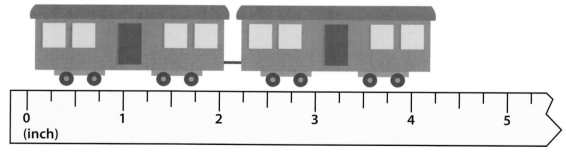

A. 4 in.   B. $4\frac{1}{4}$ in.   C. $4\frac{1}{2}$ in.   D. 5 in.

TRY IT

A ruler marked from 0 to 6 inches.

0 (inch) 1 2 3 4 5 6

7. Estimate the length of the dollar bill.

A. about 3 in.   B. about 5 in.

C. about 10 in.   D. about 15 in.

8. Estimate the length of the milk bottle.

A. about $3\frac{1}{2}$ in.   B. about 4 in.

C. about $4\frac{1}{2}$ in.   D. about 5 in.

T R Y   I T

9. Which is the most accurate estimate of the length of the carrot?

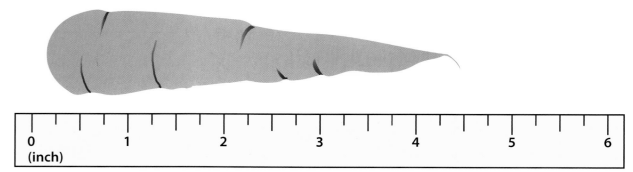

A. about 3 in.

B. about $3\frac{1}{2}$ in.

C. about 4 in.

D. about $4\frac{1}{2}$ in.

10. What is the length of the eraser?

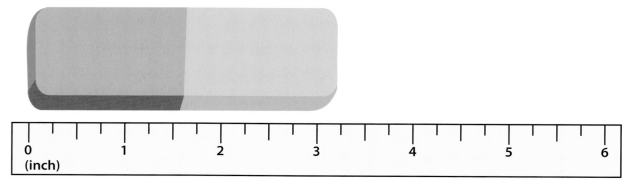

A. $2\frac{3}{4}$ in.

B. 3 in.

C. $3\frac{1}{4}$ in.

D. $3\frac{1}{2}$ in.

11. What is the length of the spoon?

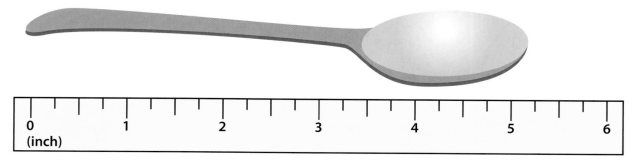

A. $5\frac{1}{4}$ in.

B. $5\frac{1}{2}$ in.

C. $5\frac{3}{4}$ in.

D. 6 in.

TRY IT

12. What is the length of the flower?

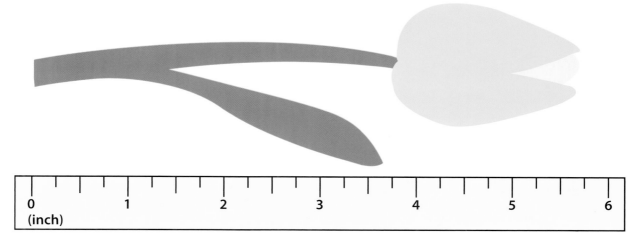

A. $5\frac{3}{4}$ in.   B. 6 in.

C. $6\frac{1}{4}$ in.   D. $6\frac{1}{2}$ in.

13. What is the length of the remote control?

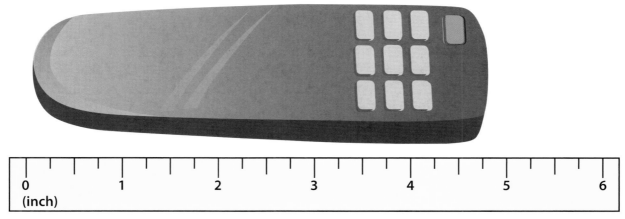

A. $4\frac{1}{4}$ in.   B. $4\frac{1}{2}$ in.

C. $4\frac{3}{4}$ in.   D. $5\frac{1}{4}$ in.

T R Y   I T

14. What is the length of the caterpillar?

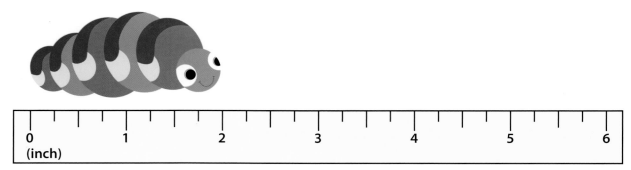

A. 2 in.

B. $2\frac{1}{4}$ in.

C. $2\frac{1}{2}$ in.

D. $2\frac{3}{4}$ in.

15. What is the height of the doll?

A. $5\frac{1}{4}$ in.

B. $5\frac{1}{2}$ in.

C. $5\frac{3}{4}$ in.

D. $6\frac{3}{4}$ in.

TRY IT

Tell Time in Minutes

Show and Tell Time

Match the time to a clock.

Time	Clock
1. Alexander went to his chess club at 8 minutes before 4.	**A.**
2. Serena practiced her violin at 23 minutes after 7.	**B.**
3. Winnie went outside with her dog at 4:17.	**C.**
4. Johnny left on Saturday morning at 8:34.	**D.**

TRY IT

Choose the answer.

5. What time is shown on this clock?

   A. 8:47

   B. 8:51

   C. 8:53

   D. 9:53

6. What time is shown on this clock?

   A. 4:36

   B. 5:37

   C. 7:04

   D. 7:21

7. What time is shown on this clock?

   A. 8 minutes before 2:00

   B. 8 minutes after 1:00

   C. 8 minutes before 1:00

   D. 5 minutes after 2:00

8. What time is shown on this clock?

   A. 8 minutes before 11:00

   B. 8 minutes after 11:00

   C. 8 minutes before 10:00

   D. 18 minutes after 11:00

9. What time is shown on this clock?

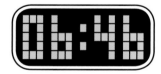

   A. 14 minutes after 6:00

   B. 4 minutes before 6:00

   C. 16 minutes before 7:00

   D. 14 minutes before 7:00

10. What time is shown on this clock?

   A. 8 minutes before 4:00

   B. 8 minutes before 5:00

   C. 2 minutes before 4:00

   D. 2 minutes before 5:00

TRY IT

11. Which clock shows the same time as this clock?

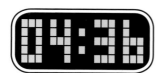

A.

B.

C.

D.

12. Which clock shows the same time as this clock?

A.

B.

C.

D.

TRY IT

13. Which clock shows the same time as this clock?

A.

B.

C.

D.

14. Which clock shows the same time as this clock?

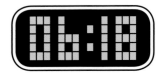

A.

B.

C.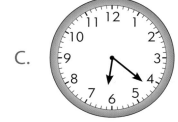

D.

TRY IT

MEASUREMENT: LENGTH AND TIME

TELL TIME IN MINUTES

Determine Elapsed Time in Minutes

How Much Time?

Write the elapsed time.

1. Billy starts building a model airplane at 1:00 p.m. and finishes at 5:32 p.m. How long does it take Billy to build the model airplane?

2. Eli leaves his house at 9:45 a.m. and returns at 3:22 p.m. How long is Eli away from home?

Find the end time.

3. Gina spends 1 hour and 47 minutes reading a book. She starts reading the book at 6:45 p.m. What time does she stop reading?

4. Josie goes to sleep at 10:10 p.m. She sleeps for 9 hours and 40 minutes. What time does Josie wake up?

Choose the answer.

5. It takes Jeff 23 minutes to bike to his soccer practice. He left his house at 10:45. What time will Jeff arrive at his soccer practice?
   - A. 10:08
   - B. 10:23
   - C. 11:08
   - D. 11:58

6. Sam's family left their house at 11:15 a.m. It took them 2 hours and 13 minutes to drive to the beach. What time did Sam's family get to the beach?
   - A. 1:02 a.m.
   - B. 1:02 p.m.
   - C. 1:28 a.m.
   - D. 1:28 p.m.

TRY IT

7. The Flores family was taking a road trip. They left their home at 9:10. This clock shows when they arrived at their final destination.

How long did the Flores family road trip last?

A. 2 hours and 13 minutes

B. 3 hours and 13 minutes

C. 2 hours and 23 minutes

D. 3 hours and 23 minutes

8. It takes Karina 25 minutes to walk to the park from her house. She leaves her house at 2:45 p.m. Which clock shows when Karina will arrive at the park?

A.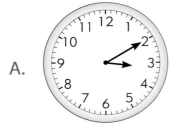

B.

C.

D.

TRY IT

Elapsed Time on a Calendar
Elapsed Time Between Days

Worked Examples

You can find elapsed time in days when the start date is in one month and the end date is in the next month. You simply add the days from each month.

PROBLEM The winter break begins on January 28 and ends on February 3. How long is the winter break?

SOLUTION 1

1 Count the winter break days in January. January has 31 days. Winter break starts on January 28. Start counting on January 29. Count January 29, 30, and 31 to get 3 days in January.

2 Count the days of winter break in February. Since the break ends on February 3, there are 3 days of winter break in February.

3 Add the number of elapsed days in January and February. $3 + 3 = 6$

SOLUTION 2

1 Subtract the number for the start date (28) from the total number of days in January (31) to find the number of winter break days in January: $31 - 28 = 3$. There are 3 winter break days in January.

2 Add the number for the end date, February 3, for the number of days in February. There are 3 days of winter break in February.

3 Add the number of elapsed days in January and February. $3 + 3 = 6$

ANSWER Winter break is 6 days long.

LEARN

Solve. Explain how you solved the problem.

1. The King family left for vacation on May 25. They plan to come home on June 8. How long will the King family be on vacation?

2. Ron had his first football practice on September 15. If today is October 20, how many days have passed since Ron's first football practice?

3. The spring sale begins on March 11 and ends on April 4. How long is the sale?

4. Winnie went to camp on July 20. She came home on August 7. How long was Winnie at camp?

5. The museum holiday shop opened on November 24. Rosa went to the store on December 18. How long had the shop been open before Rosa went to it?

LEARN

Elapsed Time on a Calendar

Number of Days

Read the problem and answer the question.

1. The farmers' market started selling strawberries on June 12. If it is June 29, how many days have passed since the market started selling strawberries?

2. Mrs. Lee left on April 28 for a business trip. She returned home on May 10. How long was the business trip?

APRIL						
Sunday	Monday	Tuesday	Wednesday	Thursday	Friday	Saturday
		1	2	3	4	5
6	7	8	9	10	11	12
13	14	15	16	17	18	19
20	21	22	23	24	25	26
27	28	29	30			

MAY						
Sunday	Monday	Tuesday	Wednesday	Thursday	Friday	Saturday
				1	2	3
4	5	6	7	8	9	10
11	12	13	14	15	16	17
18	19	20	21	22	23	24
25	26	27	28	29	30	31

3. Winnie had her first soccer practice on August 23. The first game is September 8. How many days will pass between the first practice and the first game?

4. A store opened on June 12. Adriana first went to the store on June 21. How long had the store been open before Adriana went to it?

5. Maria planted some sunflower seeds on May 15. The flowers reached 2 feet tall on June 4. How long did it take the sunflowers to grow 2 feet?

T R Y   I T

Choose the answer.

6. Jody had her first baseball practice on May 3. Today is May 19. How many days have passed since Jody's first baseball practice?

   A. 15 days   B. 16 days

   C. 21 days   D. 22 days

7. Peter finished his science project on March 15. The project was due on March 21. How early was Peter in finishing his science project?

   A. 3 days   B. 4 days

   C. 5 days   D. 6 days

8. Jeremy last went to the zoo on June 25. Today is July 13. How many days has it been since Jeremy last went to the zoo?

🌼 JUNE 🌼

Sunday	Monday	Tuesday	Wednesday	Thursday	Friday	Saturday
					1	2
3	4	5	6	7	8	9
10	11	12	13	14	15	16
17	18	19	20	21	22	23
24	25	26	27	28	29	30

🌼 JULY 🌼

Sunday	Monday	Tuesday	Wednesday	Thursday	Friday	Saturday
1	2	3	4	5	6	7
8	9	10	11	12	13	14
15	16	17	18	19	20	21
22	23	24	25	26	27	28
29	30	31				

   A. 12 days   B. 13 days

   C. 17 days   D. 18 days

TRY IT

Capacity

Tools and Units to Measure Capacity

Circle the tools or units that match the description.

1. Tools that measure capacity, or liquid volume:

thermometer	tablespoon	scale
measuring cup	teaspoon	ruler

2. English units of measure and metric units of measure:

teaspoons	quarts	cups
tablespoons	gallons	pints
milliliters	liters	

Choose the answer.

3. Sheela measured the amount of juice a pitcher would hold. Which unit of measure did she use?

   A. feet   B. cups

   C. miles   D. pounds

4. Manny wanted to measure the capacity of the gasoline tank in his car. Which unit would be the most appropriate for him to use?

   A. liter   B. kilogram

   C. kilometer   D. centimeter

T R Y   I T

5. Lena washed a load of clothes. How much water did the washing machine likely hold when it was full?

    A. 30 fluid ounces   B. 30 cups

    C. 30 pints   D. 30 gallons

6. How much liquid is the spoon most likely to hold?

    A. 15 liters   B. 15 meters

    C. 15 centimeters   D. 15 milliliters

7. The capacity of which container is most likely measured in gallons?

A.
teapot

B.
bowl

C.
mug

D.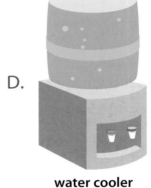
water cooler

8. Which has a capacity of about 1 quart?

A.
mug

B.
pitcher

C.
toy bathtub

D.
spoon

TRY IT

9. Marilyn's plant needs 8 fluid ounces of water twice a week. Which is the **best** tool to use to measure the amount of water the plant needs for one week?

A. ruler

B. balance

C. thermometer

D. measuring cup

10. Clarissa is baking a cake. She needs to measure some milk for the batter. Which measurement tool should Clarissa use?

A.

measuring cup

B.

scale

C.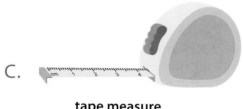

tape measure

D.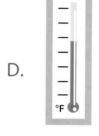

thermometer

11. What should a measuring cup be used to measure?

A. temperature

B. liquid volume

C. weight

D. height

TRY IT

Measure to the Nearest Liter

Identify Volume

Choose the answer.

1. Which item holds about 1 milliliter of water?

   A.

   large pitcher

   B.

   teaspoon

   C.

   toy bathtub

2. Which item holds about 5 liters of water?

   A.

   coffee mug

   B.

   small
   measuring cup

   C.

   bucket

3. Which item holds about 100 liters of water?

   A.

   vase

   B.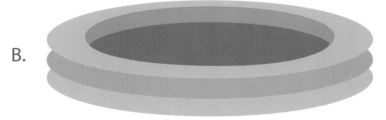

   small wading pool

   C.

   drinking cup

TRY IT

4. About how much water is in this fish tank?

A. 40 mL B. 40 L

C. 400 L D. 4,000 L

5. About how much lemonade is in this pitcher?

A. 2 L B. 20 L

C. 200 L D. 2,000 L

6. About how much water is in this sink?

A. 2 L B. 20 L

C. 200 L D. 2,000 L

7. How much juice is in this bottle?

A. 1 L B. 2 L

C. 3 L D. 4 L

8. How much pudding is in this bowl?

A. 1 L B. 2 L

C. 3 L D. 4 L

9. How much juice is in this jug?

A. 1 L B. 2 L

C. 3 L D. 4 L

T R Y   I T

10. How much water is in this large pot?

A. 2 L

B. 3 L

C. 4 L

D. 5 L

11. Which of the following objects holds about 50 liters?

A.

car gas tank

B.

watering can

C.

pail

D.

drinking cup

12. During a science experiment, Christina poured water from Container 1 into Container 2 until the second container was full, as shown.

How much water is in Container 2?

A. 1 L

B. 2 L

C. 3 L

D. 4 L

Container 1

Container 2

TRY IT

English Units of Capacity

Estimate Capacity in English Units

Match the capacity to the container.

Container	Capacity
1.	A. less than 1 cup
2.	B. about 1 cup
3.	C. more than 1 cup

Container	Capacity
4.	A. about 1 gallon
5.	B. less than 1 gallon
6.	C. more than 1 gallon

TRY IT

Choose the answer.

7. A juice box contains about how much liquid?

   A. 1 fl oz
   B. 1 gal
   C. 1 qt
   D. 1 c

8. Which object would hold about 4 cups of liquid when completely filled?

   A. baby bottle
   B. large fish tank
   C. kitchen sink
   D. pitcher

9. Which object would hold about 3 cups of liquid when completely filled?

   A. bottle of ketchup
   B. kitchen sink
   C. cooler
   D. gas tank

10. How much milk is left in this container?

   A. 4 c
   B. 8 c
   C. 12 c
   D. 16 c

11. How much pudding is in this bowl?

   A. 1 c
   B. 3 c
   C. 2 c
   D. 4 c

TRY IT

12. Maria has two pitchers for juice. She poured 10 cups of juice in one pitcher and the rest in the other pitcher as shown.

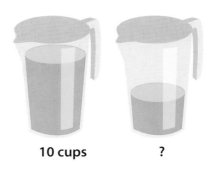

10 cups   ?

About how many cups of juice did Maria pour into the second pitcher?

A. 1 c

B. 4 c

C. 7 c

D. 9 c

13. Denise filled three water balloons using 9 cups of water. Blair filled two balloons using 7 cups of water. Sam did not record the amount of water he used to fill his three balloons.

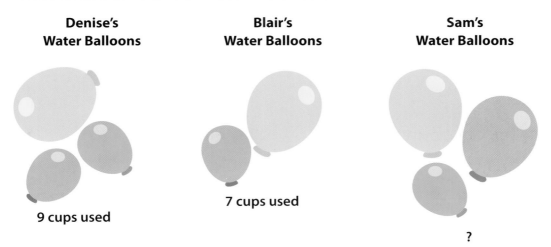

Denise's Water Balloons

Blair's Water Balloons

Sam's Water Balloons

9 cups used

7 cups used

?

Which measure is closest to the amount of water Sam used to fill his water balloons?

A. 6 c

B. 8 c

C. 12 c

D. 20 c

T R Y   I T

Measure in Grams

Metric Units of Mass

Write the abbreviation.

1. gram

2. kilogram

Write the object's mass in grams.

3. What is the mass of the loaf of bread?

4. What is the mass of the pencil?

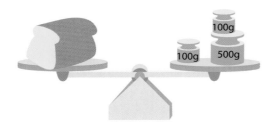

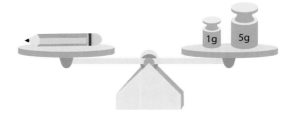

Choose the answer.

5. Which has a mass of about 1 gram?

   A. fourth-grade student

   B. paper clip

   C. automobile

   D. textbook

6. What is the approximate mass of a can of soup?

   A. 35 g

   B. 35 kg

   C. 350 g

   D. 350 kg

7. Which has a mass of about 5 grams?

   A. car   B. book   C. nickel   D. dog

TRY IT

8. Which has a mass of about 50 grams?

A.

B.

C.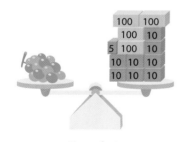

D.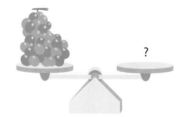

9. What is the mass of the candle?

A. 50 g

B. 55 g

C. 56 g

D. 57 g

10. David found the mass, in grams, of two bunches of grapes. The mass of Bunch 1 was 485 grams. Which estimate is closest to the mass of Bunch 2?

Bunch 1

Bunch 2

A. 500 g

B. 800 g

C. 1,000 g

D. 2,800 g

TRY IT

Measure Weight in Ounces and Pounds

Estimate and Measure Weight

Write the abbreviation.

1. ounces

Write the object's weight in ounces.

2. What is the weight of this pineapple?

3. What is the weight of this bar of soap?

4. What is the weight of this golf ball?

TRY IT

Choose the answer.

5. Which of the following objects is heavier than 1 ounce?

A.
slice of bread

B.
4 pennies

C.
grapes

D.
soccer ball

6. Which is the best estimate of the weight of a snack-size bag of dried fruit?

   A. 300 oz   B. 3 oz

   C. 3 lb   D. 30 lb

7. Which object has a weight of approximately 1 ounce?

   A. hockey puck   B. book

   C. kitten   D. strawberry

8. Which object has a weight of approximately 1 ounce?

   A. slice of bread   B. fish tank

   C. refrigerator   D. lunch box

9. Which is the **best** estimate of the weight of a can of peas?

   A. 1 oz   B. 15 oz

   C. 150 oz   D. 5 lb

T R Y   I T

10. Which object weighs about 4 ounces?

A.

cup of applesauce

B.

hardcover book

C.

wooden frame

D.

flower in pot

11. Which object weighs about 14 ounces?

A.

toothpick

B.

big potato

C.

toothbrush

D.

comb

12. Which object weighs about 4 ounces?

A. television

B. basketball

C. pear

D. strawberry

TRY IT

Unit Conversions

Convert Units of Measure

Worked Examples

You can write an expression and a number sentence to convert one unit of measure to another.

PROBLEM 1 Write an expression and a number sentence to show how many inches there are in 5 feet.

SOLUTION

1 Look for the two measures in the problem.
The measures are inches and feet.

2 Identify what you need to find to solve the problem.
You need to find the number of inches in 5 feet.

3 Write the conversion number sentence that compares the two measures. The number sentence 12 inches = 1 foot compares the measures.

4 Identify which unit of measure you have. Is it the larger unit or the smaller unit? You have 5 feet and you want to know how many inches that is. You're changing from larger units (feet) to smaller units (inches).

5 Decide whether you will multiply or divide. Multiply if you're changing larger units to smaller units. You will have more of the smaller units. Multiply the number of units you're converting (5) by the number of smaller units (12) in the conversion number sentence.

Multiply. You have 5 feet, and you know there are 12 inches in each foot. So multiply 5×12 to find the total number of inches.

L E A R N

6 Write the expression and number sentence.
Expression: 5×12
Number sentence: $5 \times 12 = ?$

ANSWER $5 \times 12 = 60$
There are 60 inches in 5 feet.

PROBLEM 2 Write an expression and a number sentence to show how many yards equal 12 feet.

SOLUTION

1 Look for the two measures in the problem.
The measures are feet and yards.

2 Identify what you need to find to solve the problem.
You need to find the number of yards in 12 feet.

3 Write the conversion number sentence that compares the two measures. The number sentence 3 feet = 1 yard compares the measures.

4 Identify which unit of measure you have. Is it the larger unit or the smaller unit? You have 12 feet, and you want to know how many yards that is. You're changing from smaller units (feet) to larger units (yards).

5 Decide if you will multiply or divide. Divide if you're changing smaller units to larger units. You will have fewer of the larger units. Divide the number of units you're converting (12) by the number of smaller units (3) in the conversion number sentence.

Divide. You have 12 feet, and you know that 3 feet equal 1 yard. So divide $12 \div 3$ to find the number of yards.

6 Write the expression and number sentence.
Expression: $12 \div 3$
Number sentence: $12 \div 3 = ?$

ANSWER $12 \div 3 = 4$
4 yards equal 12 feet.

Write the expression.

1. Write an expression to show how many ounces are in 7 pounds. (16 ounces = 1 pound)

2. Write an expression to show how many items are in 3 dozen. (12 items = 1 dozen)

Write the number sentence.

3. Write a number sentence to show how many quarts are in 16 pints. (2 pints = 1 quart)

4. Write a number sentence to show how many minutes are in 5 hours. (60 minutes = 1 hour)

5. Write a number sentence to show how many dollars are equal to 24 quarters. (4 quarters = 1 dollar)

LEARN

Unit Conversions

Write the Conversion

Write the measurement conversion. Use the conversion to solve the problem.

1. How many weeks are in 1 year?

2. How many quarters are in $5?

3. Curtis bought 36 eggs. How many dozen eggs did he buy?

Choose the answer.

4. Which expression shows how many inches are in 6 feet? (12 in. = 1 ft)

   A. 6×12

   B. $12 \div 6$

5. Which number sentence shows how many quarts are in 10 pints? (2 pt = 1 qt)

   A. $10 \times 2 = ?$

   B. $10 \div 2 = ?$

6. Sally is 3 feet tall. Which number sentence could be used to find how tall Sally is in inches? (12 in. = 1 ft)

   A. $3 \times 12 = ?$

   B. $3 + 12 = ?$

   C. $10 - 3 = ?$

   D. $3 \times 10 = ?$

7. A desk is 2 meters wide. Which number sentence could be used to figure out how wide the desk is in centimeters? (100 cm = 1 m)

   A. $2 + 2 = ?$

   B. $2 \times 100 = ?$

   C. $100 + 2 = ?$

   D. $100 - 2 = ?$

8. Ken is serving juice at his party. Each juice bottle contains 2 liters of juice. Which number sentence will tell how many milliliters of juice are in each bottle? (1,000 mL = 1 L)

   A. $2 \times 1,000 = ?$

   B. $1,000 \div 2 = ?$

   C. $2 \times 100 = ?$

   D. $100 \div 2 = ?$

TRY IT

9. Mindy needed 8 cups of strawberries. Which number sentence could be used to figure out how many pints of strawberries Mindy should buy? (2 c = 1 pt)

A. $8 + 2 = ?$

B. $8 \div 2 = ?$

C. $8 - 2 = ?$

D. $8 \times 2 = ?$

10. Susie filled up her car with 48 quarts of gas. Which number sentence could be used to figure out how many gallons of gas Susie put into her car? (4 qt = 1 gal)

A. $48 \times 4 = ?$

B. $48 \div 4 = ?$

C. $48 + 4 = ?$

D. $48 - 4 = ?$

11. A bag of sugar has a mass of 5 kilograms. Which expression could be used to figure out the mass of the sugar in grams? (1,000 g = 1 kg)

A. $5 \times 1,000$

B. $1,000 \div 5$

C. 5×100

D. $100 \div 5$

12. The baker said the bread would stay fresh for 7 days. Which number sentence could be used to figure out how many hours that is? (24 hours = 1 day)

A. $24 - 7 = ?$

B. $24 \div 7 = ?$

C. $24 + 7 = ?$

D. $7 \times 24 = ?$

13. In 2 years Andrew will take a trip around the world. Which number sentence could be used to figure out how many months will pass before Andrew takes his trip? (12 months = 1 year)

A. $12 \times 2 = ?$

B. $12 \div 2 = ?$

C. $12 + 2 = ?$

D. $12 - 2 = ?$

14. A jar contained $8 in dimes. Which number sentence could be used to figure out how many dimes are in the jar? (10 dimes = $1)

A. $10 + 8 = ?$

B. $10 \div 8 = ?$

C. $10 \times 8 = ?$

D. $10 - 8 = ?$

TRY IT

Measurement Conversions (A)

Conversion Stories

Worked Examples

You can multiply or divide to solve a unit-conversion story problem.

PROBLEM 1 Ron set the microwave for 2 minutes. How many seconds are in 2 minutes?

SOLUTION

1 Look for the two measures in the problem. The measures are minutes and seconds.

2 Identify what you need to find to solve the problem. You need to find the number of seconds in 2 minutes.

3 Write the conversion number sentence that compares the two measures. The number sentence 60 seconds = 1 minute compares the measures.

4 Identify which unit of measure you have. Is it the larger unit or the smaller unit? You have 2 minutes and you want to know how many seconds that is. You're changing from larger units (minutes) to smaller units (seconds).

5 Decide whether you will multiply or divide. You have 2 minutes, and you know that there are 60 seconds in each minute. Multiply if you're changing larger units to smaller units.

Multiply 2 × 60 to find the total number of seconds.

6 Write the number sentence to convert the minutes to seconds.

Number sentence: $2 \times 60 = ?$

ANSWER $2 \times 60 = 120$

There are 120 seconds in 2 minutes.

PROBLEM 2 Mrs. Murphy had 64 quarters. She threw 12 quarters into a fountain. How many dollars does Mrs. Murphy have left in quarters?

SOLUTION

1 Look for the two measures in the problem. The measures are quarters and dollars.

2 Identify what you need to find to solve the problem. You need to find how many dollars Mrs. Murphy has left in quarters. But first you need to find out how many quarters Mrs. Murphy had after she threw 12 quarters into the fountain. Subtract the number of quarters Mrs. Murphy threw into the fountain (12) from the number of quarters she started with (64).

$64 - 12 = 52$

Mrs. Murphy has 52 quarters.

3 Write the conversion number sentence that compares the two measures. The number sentence 4 quarters = 1 dollar compares the measures

4 Identify which unit of measure you have. Is it the larger unit or the smaller unit? You have 52 quarters and you want to know how many dollars that is. You're changing from smaller units (quarters) to larger units (dollars).

LEARN

5 Decide whether you will multiply or divide. Divide if you're changing smaller units to larger units. You will have fewer of the larger units.

You will divide. You have 52 quarters, and you know that 4 quarters are equal to 1 dollar.

6 Write the number sentence to convert the quarters to dollars.

Number sentence: $52 \div 4 = ?$

ANSWER $52 \div 4 = 13$

Mrs. Murphy has $13 left in quarters.

Solve.

1. Rosa has 12 feet of ribbon. How many yards of ribbon does Rosa have? (3 ft = 1 yd)

2. The mass of a pumpkin is 3 kilograms. What is the mass of the pumpkin in grams? (1k = 1,000 g)

3. Serena has 3 dozen muffins to sell at a bake sale. She sells 1 dozen. How many muffins does Serena have left? (1 dozen = 12 items)

4. Alexander fills a bucket with 20 quarts of water. He spills 4 quarts. How many gallons of water are left in the bucket? (4 qt = 1 gal)

LEARN

Measurement Conversions (A)

Convert and Solve

Solve.

1. 10 dimes equal 1 dollar. How many dimes equal 6 dollars?

2. There are 2 pints in 1 quart. How many quarts equal 14 pints?

3. Cole's cat Bix is 3 years old. He wants to figure out Bix's age in months. There are 12 months in a year.

   How many months are in 3 years?

4. Katrina has 4 liters of juice to serve at her party. Her mom brings home another liter of juice.

   How many milliliters of juice does Katrina have altogether? (1,000 mL = 1 L)

5. Jackson has 600 centimeters of rope. He uses 100 centimeters of rope as a lasso.

   How many meters of rope does he have left? (100 cm = 1 m)

6. Beth bought 3 dozen eggs. How many eggs did she buy? (12 items = 1 dozen)

7. Tiffany biked 2 km. How many meters did she bike? (1,000 m = 1 km)

8. 4 hours is equivalent to how many minutes? (60 minutes = 1 hour)

9. How many quarts are in 24 pints? (2 pints = 1 quart)

TRY IT

Choose the answer.

10. How many quarters are equal to 4 dollars?
    (4 quarters = $1)

    A. 1 B. 4

    C. 16 D. 20

11. Jan is riding her bike 9 kilometers to her grandmother's house. She has biked 2 kilometers already.

    How many more meters does Jan have to bike?
    (1,000 m = 1 km)

    A. 70 m B. 700 m

    C. 7,000 m D. 70,000 m

12. Jorge found two jars filled with pennies. One jar held $2 and the other jar held $3.

    How many pennies did Jorge find? (100 pennies = $1)

    A. 5 B. 20

    C. 500 D. 1,000

13. Della has 3 pounds of apples for a fruit salad. Each apple weighs about 6 ounces. Della knows there are 16 ounces in a pound.

    How many apples does Della have for the fruit salad?

    A. 2 B. 8

    C. 24 D. 48

TRY IT

Measurement Conversions (B)

Solve and Convert Answers

Worked Examples

You can solve two-step story problems with measurement conversions.

PROBLEM 1 Mrs. Ford baked 24 blueberry muffins and 12 corn muffins. How many dozen muffins did Mrs. Ford bake altogether?

SOLUTION

1 Look for the two measures in the problem. The measures are single muffins and dozen.

2 Identify what you need to find to solve the problem. You need to find how many dozen muffins Mrs. Ford baked altogether. But first you need to find how many single muffins she baked.

3 Add the single items in the story problem. There are 24 blueberry muffins and 12 corn muffins. $24 + 12 = 36$

4 Write the conversion number sentence that compares the two measures. 12 items = 1 dozen

5 Identify which unit of measure you have. Is it the larger unit or the smaller unit? You have 36 muffins and you want to know how many dozen muffins that is. You're changing from smaller units (single muffins) to larger units (dozens).

6 Decide whether you will multiply or divide. You have 36 muffins, and you know that there are 12 muffins in a dozen. So divide $36 \div 12$ to find the total number of muffins.

L E A R N

7 Write the number sentence to convert the single muffins to dozens. $36 \div 12 = ?$

ANSWER $36 \div 12 = 3$; Mrs. Ford baked 3 dozen muffins.

PROBLEM 2 The trip to Florida takes 22 hours. Ali's family has traveled for 19 hours so far. How many more minutes do they still have to travel?

SOLUTION

1 Look for the two measures in the problem. The measures are hours and minutes.

2 Identify what you need to find to solve the problem. You need to find how many more minutes Ali's family has to travel. But first you need to find out how many hours they have to travel.

3 Subtract the number of hours Ali's family has traveled (19) from the total hours the trip takes (22). $22 - 19 = 3$

4 Write the conversion number sentence that compares the two measures in this problem. 1 hour = 60 minutes

5 Identify which unit of measure you have. Is it the larger unit or the smaller unit? You have 3 hours and you want to know how many minutes that is. You're changing from larger units (hours) to smaller units (minutes).

6 Decide whether you will multiply or divide. You have 3 hours and you know there are 60 minutes in each hour. So multiply 3×60 to find the number of minutes in 3 hours.

7 Write the number sentence to convert 3 hours to minutes. $3 \times 60 = ?$

ANSWER $3 \times 60 = 180$; Ali's family still has to travel 180 minutes.

LEARN

Solve.

1. Sharon collected 46 nickels. Mark collected 34 nickels. How many dollars did they collect altogether? (20 nickels = $1)

2. The water container holds 5 liters. The soccer team drank 3 liters. How many milliliters of water are left? (1 L = 1,000 mL)

3. Theo mixes 6 pints of fruit juice and 3 pints of soda water to make one batch of punch. How many cups are in one batch of punch? (1 pt = 2 c)

4. The distance between the start and finish of the turtle race is 400 centimeters. Winnie's turtle has crawled 200 centimeters so far. How many more meters does Winnie's turtle need to crawl to reach the finish line? (100 cm = 1 m)

LEARN

Measurement Conversions (B)

Measurement Problems

Write the number sentence.

1. There are 24 hours in one day. The baby is 72 hours old. How many days old is the baby?

2. There are 16 ounces in 1 pound. The baby weighs 8 pounds. How many ounces does the baby weigh?

Solve.

3. There are 4 quarters in $1. Jimmy wants to spend $5 at the arcade. How many quarters should he bring?

4. There are 3 feet in 1 yard. Mr. Porter has 30 feet of fencing. He uses 21 feet to make a chicken pen. How many yards of fencing does Mr. Porter have left?

5. $6 is the same as how many quarters? (4 quarters = $1)

6. Adrienne bought 6 quarts of milk. How many pints of milk did Adrienne buy? (2 pt = 1 qt)

Choose the answer.

7. The recipe calls for 16 fluid ounces of buttermilk and 8 fluid ounces of regular milk. How many cups of milk are needed? (8 fl oz = 1 c)

   A. 3 c   B. 24 c   C. 64 c   D. 192 c

TRY IT

8. Marcus is taking two books back to the library. Each book has a mass of 2 kg. What is the total mass of the books, in grams? (1,000 g = 1 kg)

    A. 200 g   B. 400 g   C. 1,000 g   D. 4,000 g

9. Dave is planning to run 3 kilometers and then walk 4 kilometers. How many meters is Dave planning to cover? (1,000 m = 1 km)

    A. 100 m   B. 1,000 m   C. 700 m   D. 7,000 m

10. Theresa bought 4 dozen brown eggs and 1 dozen white eggs. What is the total number of eggs that Theresa bought? (12 items = 1 dozen)

    A. 48   B. 60   C. 72   D. 120

TRY IT

Analyze Story Problems (B)

Plan a Solution Strategy

Worked Examples

You can analyze a story problem and devise a plan to solve it.

PROBLEM Joanna lives 4 blocks from her friend's house. On the day she visited her friend, she rode her bike 14 blocks. The next day, she rode 3 times as many blocks. How many blocks did Joanna ride in all?

SOLUTION

1 Understand the problem. **The question:** How many blocks did Joanna ride in all? **Facts you need:** Joanna rode her bike 14 blocks the first day. She rode 3 times that many blocks the second day. **Facts you do NOT need:** Joanna lives 4 blocks from her friend's house.

2 Decide on a strategy.
- Make a table.
- Write a number sentence.

3 Make a plan (see Answer).

ANSWER The plan to solve the problem is

Step 1: Make a table showing the number of blocks Joanna rode each day.

Step 2: Add the number of blocks.

Step 3: Solve. $14 + 42 = ?$ or $14 + 14 + 14 + 14 = ?$

Blocks Joanna Rode		
	First day	Second day
	14	3×14
Daily Total	14	42

$14 + 42 = ?$

Blocks Joanna Rode	
First day	Second day
14	$14 + 14 + 14$

$14 + 14 + 14 + 14 = ?$

Complete the table. Describe the plan to solve the problem.

1. Chuck puts 6 baseball cards on each page of an album. He puts cards on 57 pages and has 3 cards left over. Each card is more than 2 years old.

   How many baseball cards does Chuck have?

   Understand the Problem

The question	?
Facts I need	?
Facts I do NOT need	?

   Devise a Plan
   Multiply the number of cards per page (6) by __?__ .
   Then add __?__ .
   Write a number sentence.

2. The books on sale cost $45 for 5. The CDs on sale cost $5.75 each. Hayley buys 1 book and she has a coupon for $2.50 off.

   How much does Hayley pay for the book?

   Understand the Problem

The question	?
Facts I need	?
Facts I do NOT need	?

   Devise a Plan

   Draw a picture. Divide $45 by __?__ to get the price of 1 book.

   Take the price of 1 book and subtract __?__ for the coupon.

   Write a number sentence.

LEARN

Analyze Story Problems (B)

Understand and Plan

Explain the steps needed to solve the problem.

1. The candle store sold 169 candles on Monday and 198 candles on Tuesday. Each candle cost $3.

   How many more candles did the store sell on Tuesday than on Monday?

Choose the answer.

2. Which question is being asked in this problem?

   Jim bought 4 pounds of apples and 6 pounds of oranges. Jim bought how many more pounds of oranges than apples?

   A. What is the difference between the weight of apples Jim bought and the weight of oranges he bought?

   B. How many pounds of apples did Jim buy?

   C. How many pounds of apples and oranges combined did Jim buy?

3. Johnny is building a scratching post for his cats. He needs a piece of wood $1\frac{1}{2}$ feet long for the base and a piece of wood twice that length for the post. There are 4 pieces of carpeting on the post.

   How long a piece of wood does Johnny need to buy? Choose the correct calculation.

   A. $1\frac{1}{2} + 2$

   B. $1\frac{1}{2} + 4$

   C. $1\frac{1}{2} + 1\frac{1}{2} + 1\frac{1}{2}$

   D. $1\frac{1}{2} + 2 + 4$

TRY IT

4. Which information is necessary to solve this problem?

There were 58 blackbirds and 6 sparrows sitting in a tree. At 12:30 p.m., 26 more blackbirds landed on the tree, and 12 blackbirds flew away.

How many blackbirds were left on the tree?

A. 58 blackbirds, 26 blackbirds, 12 blackbirds

B. 58 blackbirds, 26 blackbirds, 6 sparrows, 12 blackbirds

C. 58 blackbirds, 12:30 p.m., 12 blackbirds

5. Which option shows steps that could be used to solve this problem?

Joanne drove 126 miles the first day. She drove twice as far the second day.

How far did Joanne drive in two days?

A. Add 126 and 126 and then multiply by 2.

B. Add 126 and 126 and then divide by 2.

C. Multiply 126 by 2 and then add 126.

6. Which **two** options show steps that could be used to solve this problem?

Olivia has two soup mixes in her cupboard. One mix makes 18 ounces of soup and one mix makes 24 ounces of soup. Each bowl holds 6 ounces of soup.

How many bowls of soup can Olivia make?

A. **Step 1:** Divide 18 by 6.
   Step 2: Divide 24 by 6.
   Step 3: Add the two quotients.

B. **Step 1:** Add 18 and 24.
   Step 2: Divide the sum by 6.

C. **Step 1:** Divide 18 by 6.
   Step 2: Divide 24 by 6.
   Step 3: Subtract the two quotients.

TRY IT

7. Which **two** options show steps that could be used to solve this problem?

Tickets to a concert cost $25 for adults and $13 for children.

How much would tickets cost for 3 adults and 3 children?

A. **Step 1:** Subtract $13 from $25.
Step 2: Multiply the answer by 3.

B. **Step 1:** Multiply $25 by 3.
Step 2: Multiply $13 by 3.
Step 3: Add the two products.

C. **Step 1:** Add $25 and $13.
Step 2: Multiply the answer by 3.

TRY IT

Analyze Story Problems (C)

Amusement Park Fun

Worked Examples

You can analyze a story problem and devise a plan to solve it.

PROBLEM Describe the plan to solve the problem below. The day camp counselors are taking 80 children and 12 adults to an amusement park. They have 2 buses and 3 vans. If they take only the buses and put same number of people on each bus, how many people will ride on each bus?

SOLUTION 1

1 Understand the problem.
You need to make a plan to solve the problem.
The question: How many people will ride on each bus? **Facts you need:** 80 children and 12 adults are going amusement park. They will ride in 2 buses. The same number of people will ride on each bus. **Facts you do NOT need:** They have 3 vans.

2 Decide on a strategy.
- Use logical reasoning to make a list of steps.
- Translate into a number sentence.

3 Make the plan (see Answer).

ANSWER The plan to solve the problem is
Step 1: Add $80 + 12$ to find how many people will ride on buses.
$80 + 12 = 92$
Step 2: Divide the total by 2 to find out how many will be on each bus.
Step 3: Solve. $92 \div 2 = ?$

L E A R N

SOLUTION 2

1 Understand the problem (see Solution 1).

2 Decide on a strategy.
  • Make tally charts.

3 Make the plan (see Answer).

ANSWER The plan to solve the problem is
Step 1: Make two tally charts, one for each bus.
Step 2: Make a tally mark for each child and each adult so that there are the same number of tally marks in each chart.
Step 3: Count the tally marks in one chart.

Bus 1

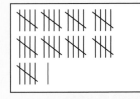

Bus 2

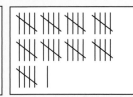

Complete the table. Describe the plan to solve the problem.

1. The campers plan to leave camp at 9:00 a.m. and return at 5:00 p.m. The puppet show is at 2:00 p.m. The drive to and from the amusement park is about 30 minutes each way.

   How much time will the campers have at the park?

Understand the Problem		
The question	**Facts I need**	**Facts I do NOT need**
?	?	?

Devise a Plan
What strategy will you use?
What steps will you follow?

2. There are 80 campers and 10 counselors. Two counselors are assigned to each group. There are 100 bottles of water. If each group has the same number of campers, how many campers are in each group?

Understand the Problem		
The question	**Facts I need**	**Facts I do NOT need**
?	?	?

Devise a Plan
What strategy will you use?
What steps will you follow?

3. The camp counselors bought 80 child tickets, 12 adult tickets, and 10 tote bags. The child tickets were $9 each, and the adult tickets were $5 each.

How much did the camp counselors spend on tickets?

Understand the Problem		
The question	**Facts I need**	**Facts I do NOT need**
?	?	?

Devise a Plan
What strategy will you use?
What steps will you follow?

LEARN

4. Counselor Tim spent $20 on 4 patches and $5.50 on snacks. Each patch cost the same amount of money.

How much did each patch cost?

Understand the Problem		
The question	**Facts I need**	**Facts I do NOT need**
?	?	?

Devise a Plan
What strategy will you use?
What steps will you follow?

5. The bus drivers drove $20\frac{1}{2}$ miles to the amusement park. They parked for 6 hours. They drove an additional $2\frac{1}{2}$ miles when they had to take a detour on the way home.

How many miles did the bus drivers drive on the way home?

Understand the Problem		
The question	**Facts I need**	**Facts I do NOT need**
?	?	?

Devise a Plan
What strategy will you use?
What steps will you follow?

LEARN

Analyze Story Problems (C)

What Are the Steps?

Explain the steps needed to solve the problem.

1. Emma picked 8 baskets of strawberries and 3 baskets of blueberries. If she put 25 strawberries in each basket, how many strawberries did she pick?

2. The market sold 35 baskets of strawberries on Saturday. On Sunday, it sold 14 baskets of strawberries and 22 baskets of blueberries. It sold each basket for $4.

   How much money did the market make selling strawberries over the two days?

3. Melissa has to drive 125 miles to the beach. She drove for 2 hours at 55 miles per hour.

   How many more miles does Melissa have to drive?

Choose the answer.

4. Which information is **not** necessary to solve this problem?

   Dale had $25 to spend on pizza. His mom gave him another $25, so he had a total of $50 to spend on pizza. He bought 2 small pizzas for $12 each and 1 large pizza for $18.

   How much change did Dale get back from his $50?

   A. the amount of money Dale got from his mom

   B. the total amount of money Dale had

   C. the price of a small pizza

   D. the price of a large pizza

TRY IT

5. Which option shows the correct steps to solve this problem?

Nina had 29 toy cars in her collection. Her grandpa gave her 4 cars and she gave away 7 cars.

How many toy cars does Nina have now?

A. Add 29 and 4, and then subtract 7.

B. Add 29 and 7, and then add 4.

C. Add 29 and 4, and then add 7.

6. Which option shows the correct steps to solve this problem?

In March, Ralph spent $48 on train fare. In April, he spent $36 on train fare. Each train ticket cost $4.

How many more tickets did Ralph buy in March than in April?

A. Divide 48 by 4, and divide 36 by 4. Subtract the smaller quotient from the larger quotient.

B. Multiply 48 by 4, and multiply 36 by 4. Add the two products.

C. Divide 48 by 4, and divide 36 by 4. Add the two quotients.

7. Which **two** options show correct steps to solve this problem?

Jean bought a soccer ball for $25.99 and a pair of socks for $3.75. She gave the cashier a $50 bill.

How much change did Jean get?

A. **Step 1:** Subtract $3.75 from $25.99.
   Step 2: Add $50.00 to the answer.

B. **Step 1:** Subtract $3.75 from $50.00.
   Step 2: Subtract $25.99 from the answer.

C. **Step 1:** Add $3.75 and $25.99.
   Step 2: Subtract the sum from $50.00.

TRY IT

8. Which **two** options show correct steps to solve this problem?

There were 2 times as many red lights as white lights on a strand of lights. There were 10 white lights on each strand.

How many red lights were on 4 strands of lights?

A. **Step 1:** Multiply 10 by 2.
Step 2: Multiply the answer by 4.

B. **Step 1:** Add 10 and 4.
Step 2: Multiply the answer by 2.

C. **Step 1:** Multiply 10 by 4.
Step 2: Multiply the answer by 2.

T R Y I T

Understand Multistep Problems

Make a Plan

Worked Examples

You can make a plan to solve a story problem. When you solve a multistep problem, you can break it into simpler parts.

PROBLEM Describe the plan to solve the problem.

Jaime went shopping and bought 3 boxes of crackers and 2 packs of cheese. Each box of crackers cost $2.30, and each pack of cheese cost $3.50. He also spent $1.29 on a birthday card for his friend. When Jaime got home, his mother said she'd pay for the food Jaime bought. How much did she have to pay?

SOLUTION

1 Understand the problem. You need to describe the plan to solve the problem. **The question:** How much did Jaime's mother pay? (She paid only for the food.) **Facts you need:** Jaime bought 3 boxes of crackers and 2 packs of cheese. Each box of crackers cost $2.30, and each pack of cheese cost $3.50. Jaime's mother said she'd pay for the food. **Facts you do NOT need:** Jaime also spent $1.29 on a birthday card.

2 Decide on a strategy.
- Use logical reasoning to break the problem into simpler parts.
- Write a number sentence for each part.

3 Make the plan (see Answer).

ANSWER

Step 1: Multiply 3 × $2.30 to find the cost of 3 boxes of crackers.
Step 2: Multiply 2 × $3.50 to find the cost 2 packs of cheese.
Step 3: Add the two products to find the total cost of the food.

LEARN

Describe the plan to solve the problem.

1. The Stewart family bicycled 46 miles each day for 5 days. Then they took a wilderness train 525 miles, arriving in Oz at 7:30 p.m.

   How far did the Stewart family travel?

Understand Multistep Problems

Stepping Through Multistep Problems

Explain the steps needed to solve the problem.

1. Serena went swimming 5 days in a row. On the first 3 days, she swam for 45 minutes each day. On days 4 and 5, she swam for 60 minutes each day. How many total minutes did Serena spend swimming during those 5 days?

Choose the answer.

2. Which option describes the calculations that could be used to solve this problem?

   Word puzzle books are on sale at 6 for $3. Pencils are on sale for $1.50 a box. Alexander bought 12 word puzzle books and a box of pencils. How much did Alexander spend?

   A. Find the cost of 12 word puzzle books.
      Subtract the price of 1 box of pencils.

   B. Find the cost of 6 word puzzle books.
      Add this to the price of 1 box of pencils.

   C. Find the cost of 12 word puzzle books.
      Add this to the price of 1 box of pencils.

3. Which option describes the simpler problems that could be used to solve this problem?

   David has 25 boys and 20 girls in his sports camp. All campers will be going on a boat trip. Each boat can hold 5 people. How many boats does David need altogether?

   A. Add the number of boys and the number of girls at the camp.
      Divide this number by the number of people who can fit in a boat.

   B. Multiply the number of boys and the number of girls at the camp.
      Subtract the number of boats.

   C. Add the number of boys and the number of girls at the camp.
      Multiply this number by the number of people who can fit in a boat.

TRY IT

4. Which option describes the calculations that could be used to solve this problem?

   The Hudson family drove 124 miles each day for 3 days. They then flew 1,254 miles. How far did the Hudson family travel?

   A. Divide 124 by 3. Then add 1,254.

   B. Multiply 124 by 3. Then add 1,254.

   C. Multiply 124 by 3. Then subtract that product from 1,254.

5. Which option describes the calculations that could be used to solve this problem?

   Janine rode 34 miles on her bike the first day of her trip. On the second day, she rode twice as far. How far did Janine ride in two days?

   A. Add 34 and 2. Then add 2 to the sum.

   B. Multiply 34 by 2. Then add 34.

   C. Divide 34 by 2. Then add 2.

6. Which option describes the calculations that could be used to solve this problem?

   Noah earned $320 one week and $264 the following week. He makes $8 an hour. How many hours did Noah work in two weeks?

   A. Divide $320 by $8. Then add $264.

   B. Divide $320 by 8. Divide $264 by 8. Multiply the two quotients.

   C. Divide $320 by 8. Divide $264 by 8. Add the two quotients.

TRY IT

7. Which **two** options show the correct steps to solve this problem?

Richard bought 5 mystery books and 3 sports books.
Each book cost $4. How much money did Richard spend?

A. Multiply 5 × 3. Then add $4 to the product.

B. Add 5 and 3. Then multiply the total by $4.

C. Multiply 5 × $4. Then multiply 3 × $4. Then add the 2 products together.

TRY IT

Strategies to Solve Complex Problems

Problem-Solving Strategies

Worked Examples

You can draw a sketch and use a chart to help you solve a story problem. When you solve a multistep problem, you can break it into simpler parts.

PROBLEM Suzanne is making bracelets. She wants each bracelet to have a pattern of 2 wooden beads, then 3 red beads, then 2 gold beads. She wants to use 6 red beads on each bracelet. How many total beads does she need to make 8 bracelets?

SOLUTION

UNDERSTAND THE PROBLEM
You need to find out how many total beads it takes to make 8 bracelets. But first you need to find out how many beads are in 1 bracelet. **Facts you need:** Each bracelet has a pattern of 2 wooden beads, then 3 red beads, then 2 gold beads. Suzanne wants to use 6 red beads in each bracelet. (To use 6 red beads, Suzanne must repeat the pattern.)

DEVISE A PLAN
Decide on a strategy.
- Draw a sketch of the pattern.
- Make a chart showing the information.

Make the plan.

1 Draw a sketch of the pattern.

2 Find out how many patterns are in a bracelet that has 6 red beads and how many beads are in 1 bracelet.

3 Multiply 8 times the number of beads in 1 bracelet.

L E A R N

CARRY OUT THE PLAN

The pattern	1 bracelet	8 bracelets
2 wooden, 3 red, 2 gold ●●●●●○○ 7 beads	A single bracelet has 6 red beads, so it must have the pattern 2 times. ●●●●●○○ ●●●●●○○ 2 times 7 beads $2 \times 7 = 14$	8 times the number of beads in 1 bracelet. $8 \times 14 = 112$

LOOK BACK

Go over the problem. Make sure that the picture is drawn correctly and the beads were counted correctly. Check your calculations using a different method. For example, 8×14 can be seen as 8×10 plus 8×4, or $80 + 32 = 112$, so it checks.

ANSWER Suzanne will need 112 beads to make 8 bracelets.

Use the problem-solving plan to understand and solve the problem.

1. Suzanne wants to make some necklaces to go with her bracelets. Each necklace has a pattern of 4 red beads, 5 clear beads, then 4 black beads. She wants to use 15 clear beads on each necklace. How many **total** beads does she need to make 4 necklaces?

LEARN

You can use the guess-and-test strategy to solve a story problem. You can use a table to record your guesses and tests.

PROBLEM Maria picked flowers in the garden for her mom. She tells her mom there are 4 more roses than tulips in the vase. There are a total of 10 flowers in the vase. How many roses and tulips are in the vase?

SOLUTION

UNDERSTAND THE PROBLEM
You need to find out how how many roses and how many tulips are in the vase. **Facts you need:** There are 4 more roses than tulips. There are a total of 10 flowers.

DEVISE A PLAN
Decide on a strategy.

- Guess and test.
- Make a table of guesses.

Make the plan.

1 Make a table for guesses.

2 Guess the number of tulips, then add that number plus 4 more to see if it totals 10 flowers.

3 Keep guessing until the number of tulips plus the number of roses is equal to 10.

LEARN

CARRY OUT THE PLAN

1 Make the table.

2 Guess 2 tulips. Add 4 to 2
to get 6 roses.
$2 + 6 = 8$ flowers
The guess is too low.

3 Guess 4 tulips. Add 4 to 4
to get 8 roses.
$4 + 8 = 12$ flowers
The guess is too high.

Tulips	Roses (4 more than the number of tulips)	Total
2	6	8
4	8	12
3	7	10

4 Guess 3 tulips. Add 4 to 3 to get 7 roses.
$3 + 7 = 10$ flowers
This is the answer.

LOOK BACK

Go over the problem. Make sure the table is correct and you added
4 to each guess correctly. Make sure your totals are correct.

ANSWER There are 3 tulips and 7 roses in the vase.

Choose the answer. Use the problem-solving plan to
understand and solve the problem.

2. The florist has a total of 48 roses and tulips.
He has 18 more roses than tulips. How many roses does
the florist have?

A. 15   B. 21   C. 27   D. 33

LEARN

Strategies to Solve Complex Problems
Learn More Strategies

Worked Examples

You can find a pattern in a table to solve a story problem.

PROBLEM Marcus volunteers 9 hours every 2 weeks at the library. He made the following table to figure out how many hours he will volunteer in 8 weeks. How long will it take Marcus to volunteer 63 hours?

Week	Hours volunteered
2	9
4	18
6	27
8	36

SOLUTION

UNDERSTAND THE PROBLEM
You need to find out how long it will take Marcus to volunteer 63 hours.
Facts you need: Marcus volunteers 9 hours every 2 weeks.

DEVISE A PLAN
Decide on strategies.

- Make a table.
- Look for a pattern.

Make the plan.

1 Make a table.

2 Find the pattern in Marcus's table.

L E A R N

3 Extend the pattern until the number of hours volunteered is 63.

CARRY OUT THE PLAN

Make a table. The Week column increases by 2 with each row. The Hours Volunteered column increases by 9 with each row.

Week	Hours volunteered
2	9
4	18
6	27
8	36
10	45
12	54
14	63

LOOK BACK

Go over the problem. Make sure you answered the question asked. Make sure the table is correct and you added 9 to each row correctly. Check your answer. Notice that 63 is in the 7th row and that 7×9 is 63, so it checks.

ANSWER It will take Marcus 14 weeks to volunteer 63 hours.

Use the problem-solving plan to understand and solve the problem.

1. Marcus volunteers 9 hours every 2 weeks at the library.

   How long will it take Marcus to volunteer 90 hours?

LEARN

You can solve some story problems by solving simpler problems using a table. You can look for a pattern in that table and then use the pattern to solve the more complex problem.

PROBLEM What is the distance around 50 triangular animal pens when they are set next to each other as shown? Each side = 1 unit, and all sides are the same length.

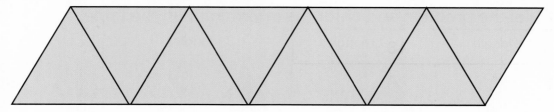

SOLUTION

UNDERSTAND THE PROBLEM

You need to find the distance around 50 triangular animal pens.
Facts you need: There are 50 triangular animal pens arranged as shown. Each side is 1 unit.

DEVISE A PLAN

Decide on strategies.

- Make a table.
- Use a model or drawing.
- Solve easier problems.
- Look for a pattern.

Make the plan.

1 Make a table showing number of triangles and the distance around.

2 Use a model or drawing and count to find the distance around 1 pen, then 2 pens, then 3 pens, and so on. Record the distances in the table.

3 Find a pattern.

4 Extend the pattern to find out what the distance around 50 triangular pens would be.

L E A R N

CARRY OUT THE PLAN

1 Make the table.

Triangles	Distance around (units)
1	
2	
3	

2 Model the problem and enter the information in the table.

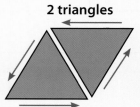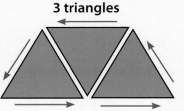

1 triangle

Distance around
is 3 units.

2 triangles

Distance around
is 4 units.

3 triangles

Distance around
is 5 units.

Triangles	Distance around (units)
1	3
2	4
3	5
4	6
5	7
6	8
7	9

3 Find the pattern. The pattern seems to be that the distance around is 2 more than the number of triangles.

4 Extend the pattern. If the distance around is 2 more than the number of triangles, then for 10 triangles the distance around should be 12. Test to see if this is true.

LEARN

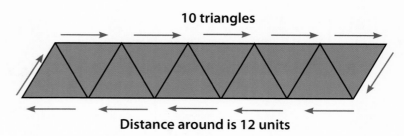

10 triangles

Distance around is 12 units

Triangles	Distance around (units)
10	12

The pattern works. For 50 triangles, the distance around would be $50 + 2 = 52$.

Triangles	Distance around (units)
50	52

LOOK BACK

Go over the problem. Make sure you answered the question asked. Make sure the table is correct. Look for another way to explain it. Notice that with 10 triangles, there are 5 sides that make the distance along the top of the figure and 5 that make the distance along the bottom. So there are $5 + 5$ sides on the top and bottom and 2 end sides that make the total distance of 12 units around the animal pens. If there were 50 triangles, there would be $25 + 25$ sides on the top and bottom and 2 end sides, for a total of 52 units around the pens.

ANSWER The distance around 50 animal pens, arranged as shown, is 52 units.

Use the problem-solving plan to understand and solve the problem.

2. What is the distance around 100 triangular animal pens when they are set next to each other as shown? Each side = 1 unit, and all sides are the same length.

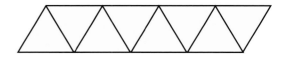

Strategies to Solve Complex Problems

Strategy Practice

Use the problem-solving plan to understand and solve the problem.

1. Darlene wanted to make necklaces by using this pattern:

   She wanted to use 8 dotted beads for each necklace. Darlene drew a diagram to figure out the total number of beads she needed for 1 necklace.

   How many beads would Darlene need to make 9 necklaces?

2. Colette's mom asked her to figure out how many oranges were in the fridge. Her mom said there were 2 more oranges than apples. The fridge had a total of 8 pieces of fruit.

   - First Colette guessed 4 oranges. Since there were 2 more oranges than apples, there would be 2 apples and a total of 6 pieces of fruit. Her guess was too low.
   - Next Colette guessed 6 oranges. That meant 4 apples and a total of 10 pieces of fruit, which was too high.
   - Then Colette guessed 5 oranges. That meant there would be 3 apples and a total of 8 pieces of fruit. Right!

   Colette then solved this math problem: Jason wants to buy a total of 56 apples and oranges. He wants 14 more oranges than apples.

   How many oranges should Jason buy?

TRY IT

Choose the answer.

3. Sean earns $15 every 2 weeks babysitting. He wants to know how much he will earn in 6 weeks.

   Sean made this table.

   How long will it take Sean to earn $135?

Week	Total amount earned
2	$15
4	$30
6	$45

   A. 7 weeks   B. 9 weeks

   C. 15 weeks   D. 18 weeks

4. Julio has 4 boxes of pencils and 2 boxes of crayons. Each box of pencils has 4 pencils, and each box of crayons has 6 crayons. Julio wants to know how many pencils and crayons he has altogether.

   He multiplied 4 × 4 to calculate that he had 16 pencils. Then he multiplied 2 × 6 to calculate that he had 12 crayons. He added the products to figure out that he had 28 crayons and pencils altogether.

   Julio got some more pencils and crayons. Now he has 6 boxes of pencils and 8 boxes of crayons.

   How many crayons and pencils does Julio have altogether?

   A. 24   B. 36   C. 48   D. 72

T R Y   I T

Story Problem Reasoning (A)

Story Problem Practice

Solve. Use a representation to explain your answer.

1. The triathlon is 20 miles long. Sarah bikes the first 12 miles and then swims 2 miles. She runs the rest of the distance.

   How far does Sarah run?

2. Rosa bought berries to make a pie. She bought 3 times as many blueberries as strawberries. She bought 8 pints of berries.

   How many pints of strawberries did she buy?

3. Johnny and his family arrived in Williamsburg, Virginia, at 1:15 p.m. They drove for 45 minutes after they stopped for lunch. Their lunch break was 20 minutes. They drove for 2 hours and 10 minutes before stopping for lunch.

   What time did they leave home?

4. There are 30 shirts in the closet. Half of the shirts are long-sleeved. Five of the shirts are polo shirts and 2 are sleeveless. The rest of the shirts are T-shirts.

   How many shirts are T-shirts?

5. There are 20 books on the shelf. Half of the books are sports stories. Three books are mystery stories and 5 are poetry. The rest of the books are fiction.

   How many books are fiction?

TRY IT

Choose the diagram that shows how to solve the problem.

6. Barbara is traveling 20 miles from her house to a cabin on an island. She drives 11 miles. She then canoes 7 miles. She has to walk the last few miles. How far does Barbara have to walk?

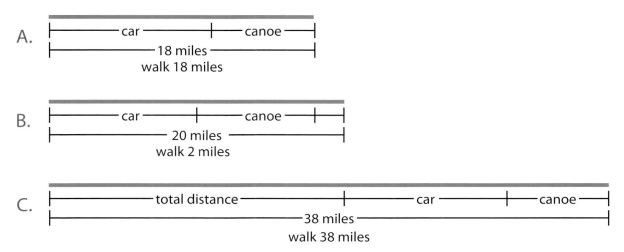

A.   car ———— canoe
      — 18 miles —
      walk 18 miles

B.   car ———— canoe
      — 20 miles —
      walk 2 miles

C.   total distance ———— car ———— canoe
      — 38 miles —
      walk 38 miles

Choose the option that explains how to solve the problem.

7. Sarah ate her lunch as soon as her piano lesson ended. She took 30 minutes to eat her lunch and then read for 20 minutes. Then her family drove for 15 minutes and arrived at her grandmother's at 12:05 p.m. What time did Sarah's piano lesson end?

    A. Work backward. Sarah started her lunch at 12:00. She ate until 12:30. She read until 12:50. She drove until 1:05. Sarah's piano lesson ended at 1:05.

    B. Work backward. Sarah left for her grandmother's at 12:20. She started to read at 12:40. She started lunch at 1:10. Sarah's piano lesson ended at 1:10.

    C. Work backward. Sarah left for her grandmother's at 11:50. She started to read at 11:30. She started lunch at 11:00. Sarah's piano lesson ended at 11:00.

T R Y   I T

Story Problem Reasoning (B)

Double Bar Graphs

Worked Examples

You can use information from a double bar graph to solve a story problem.

PROBLEM The sales office created this double bar graph to show the number of tickets sold for each performance at the Children's Theater. How many more child tickets than adult tickets were sold for Saturday's show?

SOLUTION

UNDERSTAND THE PROBLEM

You need to find how many more child tickets than adult tickets were sold for Saturday's show.

Facts you need:
The information in the Saturday bars in the double bar graph.

Facts you do NOT need:
The information in the Friday and Sunday bars.

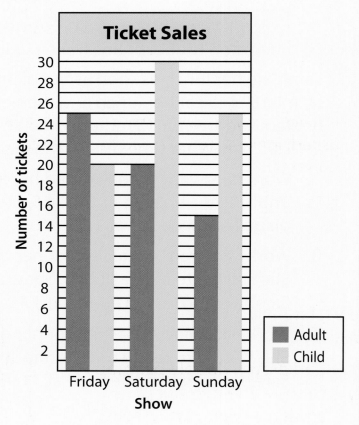

LEARN

DEVISE A PLAN

Decide on strategies.

- Apply the rules for reading double bar graphs to get the information.

- Write a number sentence to find the difference between the number of child tickets and the number of adult tickets.

Make the plan.

1 Read the double bar graph to find out how many child and adult tickets were sold for Saturday's show.

2 Write a number sentence to show the difference.

CARRY OUT THE PLAN

1 The double bar graph shows that 30 child tickets and 20 adult tickets were sold for Saturday's show.

2 $30 - 20 = 10$

LOOK BACK

Go over the problem. Make sure you answered the question asked. Make sure you read the scale of the double bar graph correctly.

ANSWER There were 10 more child tickets than adult tickets sold for Saturday's show.

Solve. Explain how you found your answer.

1. Carl drew a double bar graph to show the number of students taking art lessons. How many students are in the painting class?

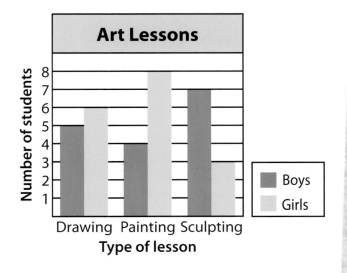

2. Katie drew this double bar graph to show sports participation. How many more boys play basketball than soccer?

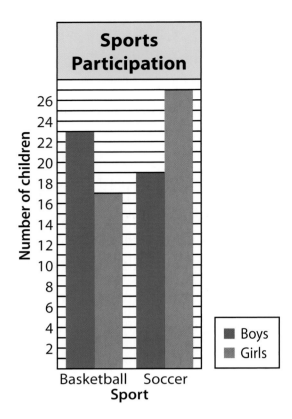

Story Problem Reasoning (B)

Graphs and Diagrams

Solve. Explain how you found your answer.

1. Ron made this Venn diagram to show the lunches the boys in his group bought at camp. How many more sandwiches were bought than slices of pizza?

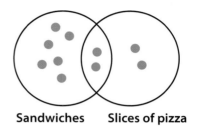

Sandwiches   Slices of pizza

Choose the option that explains how to solve the problem.

2. Josie drew this Venn diagram to show the toppings her friends like on their pizza.

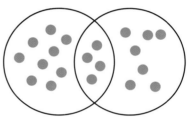

Pepperoni   Mushrooms

How many fewer people like both mushrooms and pepperoni than like only pepperoni?

A. Read the Venn diagram to learn that 7 people like both mushrooms and pepperoni and that 9 people like only pepperoni. Subtract 9 − 7 to figure out that 2 fewer people like both mushrooms and pepperoni than like only pepperoni.

B. Read the Venn diagram to learn that 4 people like both mushrooms and pepperoni and that 7 people like only pepperoni. Subtract 7 − 4 to figure out that 3 fewer people like both mushrooms and pepperoni than like only pepperoni.

C. Read the Venn diagram to learn that 4 people like both mushrooms and pepperoni and that 9 people like only pepperoni. Subtract 9 − 4 to figure out that 5 fewer people like both mushrooms and pepperoni than like only pepperoni.

TRY IT

3. Billy drew this Venn diagram to show the baseball teams his friends like.

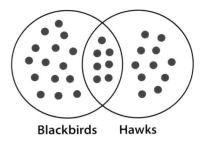

Blackbirds   Hawks

How many fewer people like both the Blackbirds and Hawks than like only the Blackbirds?

A. Read the Venn diagram to learn that 7 people like both the Blackbirds and Hawks and that 15 people like only the Blackbirds. Subtract 15 − 7 to figure out that 8 fewer people like both the Blackbirds and Hawks than like only the Blackbirds.

B. Read the Venn diagram to learn that 7 people like both the Blackbirds and Hawks and that 11 people like only the Blackbirds. Subtract 11 − 7 to figure out that 4 fewer people like both the Blackbirds and Hawks than like only the Blackbirds.

C. Read the Venn diagram to learn that 11 people like both the Blackbirds and Hawks and that 15 people like only the Blackbirds. Subtract 15 − 11 to figure out that 4 fewer people like both the Blackbirds and Hawks than like only the Blackbirds.

4. Marin drew this Venn diagram to show the ice cream her friends like.

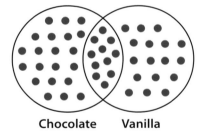

Chocolate   Vanilla

How many fewer people like chocolate and vanilla than like just vanilla?

A. Read the Venn diagram to learn that 11 people like both chocolate and vanilla and that 17 people like only vanilla. Subtract 17 − 11 to figure out that 6 fewer people like chocolate and vanilla than like just vanilla.

B. Read the Venn diagram to learn that 11 people like both chocolate and vanilla and that 21 people like only vanilla. Subtract 21 − 11 to figure out that 10 fewer people like chocolate and vanilla than like just vanilla.

C. Read the Venn diagram to learn that 17 people like both chocolate and vanilla and that 21 people like only vanilla. Subtract 21 − 17 to figure out that 4 fewer people like chocolate and vanilla than like just vanilla.

TRY IT

5. Callie drew this Venn diagram to show the subjects her friends like.

How many more people like math and science than like just science?

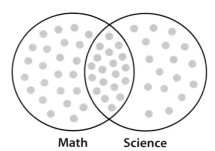

Math   Science

A. Read the Venn diagram to learn that 24 people like both math and science and that 17 like just science. Subtract 24 − 17 to figure out that 7 more people like math and science than like just science.

B. Read the Venn diagram to learn that 24 people like both math and science and that 19 like just science. Subtract 24 − 19 to figure out that 5 more people like math and science than like just science.

C. Read the Venn diagram to learn that 19 people like both math and science and that 17 like just science. Subtract 19 − 17 to figure out that 2 more people like math and science than like just science.

6. Robyn drew this double bar graph to show the number of children who took music lessons.

How many children took guitar lessons?

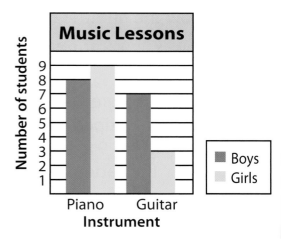

A. Read the graph to learn that 8 boys took guitar lessons and that 9 girls took guitar lessons. Add 8 + 9 to figure out that 17 children took guitar lessons.

B. Read the graph to learn that 7 boys took guitar lessons and that 3 girls took guitar lessons. Add 7 + 3 to figure out that 10 children took guitar lessons.

C. Read the graph to learn that 8 boys took guitar lessons and that 7 girls took guitar lessons. Add 8 + 7 to figure out that 15 children took guitar lessons.

T R Y   I T

7. Jackson drew this double bar graph to show the number of animals in the shelter.

How many animals were multicolored?

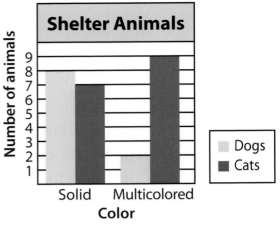

A. Read the graph to learn that 2 dogs are multicolored and 8 cats are multicolored. Add 2 + 8 to figure out that 10 animals in the shelter are multicolored.

B. Read the graph to learn that 8 dogs are multicolored and 7 cats are multicolored. Add 8 + 7 to figure out that 15 animals in the shelter are multicolored.

C. Read the graph to learn that 2 dogs are multicolored and 9 cats are multicolored. Add 2 + 9 to figure out that 11 animals in the shelter are multicolored.

8. Tara drew this double bar graph to show the number of fabric patterns.

How many patterns are blue?

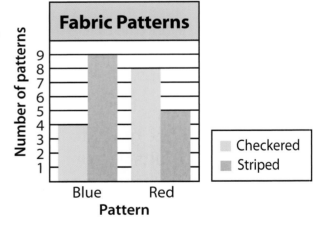

A. Read the graph to learn that 4 checkered patterns are blue and 9 striped patterns are blue. Add 4 + 9 to figure out that 13 of the patterns are blue.

B. Read the graph to learn that 4 checkered patterns are blue and 8 striped patterns are blue. Add 4 + 8 to figure out that 12 of the patterns are blue.

C. Read the graph to learn that 5 checkered patterns are blue and 9 striped patterns are blue. Add 5 + 9 to figure out that 14 of the patterns are blue.

TRY IT

Story Problem Reasoning (C)

Justify Solutions

Solve. Explain how you found the answer.

1. Ron has 100 baseball cards after going to the card show. He sold 12 cards at the card show and bought 25 cards. How many cards did Ron have before he went to the card show?

2. Winnie's soccer league assigns 2 coaches for every 12 players. This season, there are 10 coaches. How many players are there?

3. Rosa said, "I am thinking about a number. Multiply that number by 3. Then subtract 12 from the product. The answer is 33." What is Rosa's number?

4. Mrs. Chung is making fruit baskets. She uses 15 pieces of fruit for every 3 baskets she makes. If Mrs. Chung wants to make 12 baskets, how many pieces of fruit does she need?

Choose the table that shows how to solve the problem.

5. Nicole is making greeting cards. She makes 12 birthday cards and 4 get-well cards each month for 5 months. How many cards did Nicole make?

A.

Month	1	2	3	4	5
Total cards	12	24	36	48	(60)

B.

Month	1	2	3	4	5
Total cards	16	32	48	64	(80)

C.

Month	1	2	3	4	5
Total cards	4	8	12	16	(20)

TRY IT

6. The youth group planned a trip to the amusement park. There was 1 adult for every 8 children on the trip. Nine adults went to the amusement park with the group. How many children went on the trip?

A.

Adults	1	3	6	9
Children	9	18	27	(36)

B.

Adults	1	3	6	9
Children	8	16	24	(48)

C.

Adults	1	3	6	9
Children	8	24	48	(72)

7. Ichiro bought twice as many melons as pears. If he bought 12 pieces of fruit, how many melons did Ichiro buy?

A.

Pears	1	2	3	4
Melons	2	(4)	6	8
Total	3	6	9	12

B.

Pears	1	2	3	4
Melons	2	4	6	(8)
Total	3	6	9	12

C.

Pears	1	2	3	(4)
Melons	2	4	6	8
Total	3	6	9	12

Choose the option that explains how to solve the problem.

8. Eve said, "I am thinking of a number. Add 17 to this number. Multiply the sum by 3. The answer is 78." What is Eve's number?

   A. Work backward. Start with 78. Divide by 3 and get 26. Subtract 17 and get 9. Eve started with the number 9.

   B. Work backward. Start with 78. Divide by 3 and get 26. Add 17 and get 43. Eve started with the number 43.

   C. Work backward. Start with 17. Multiply by 11 and get 187. Add 78 and get 265. Eve started with the number 265.

TRY IT

Explain Solutions to Problems

Explain the Steps

Worked Examples

You can use a Venn diagram to solve and explain the solution to a story problem.

PROBLEM This weekend, Nick's baseball team gets their uniforms. The coach has asked the players to pick a two-digit number between 1 and 100 to go on their uniform. Nick wants his number to be a multiple of 5 and a multiple of 6. What numbers could be on Nick's uniform?

SOLUTION

UNDERSTAND THE PROBLEM

You need to find what numbers could be on Nick's uniform. You need to find two-digit numbers that are multiples of 5 and multiples of 6. **Facts you need:** The numbers are two-digit numbers. The numbers must be multiples of 5 and multiples of 6. **Facts you do NOT need:** The numbers are between 1 and 100. (All two-digit numbers are between 1 and 100.)

DEVISE A PLAN

Decide on a strategy.

- Draw a diagram.
- Make an organized list.

Make the plan

1 Draw a Venn diagram with two overlapping circles. Label one circle "Multiples of 5," and label the other circle "Multiples of 6."

L E A R N

2 Count by 5s to 100. Using a pencil, write the multiples of 5 in the circle labeled for 5s. Then count by 6s to 100. Write the multiples of 6 in the 6s circle. Find the numbers that are multiples of both 5 and 6. Write them in the overlapping section. Make sure that each number is only on the chart 1 time.

3 Make a list of the numbers that are multiples of both 5 and 6. (the numbers in the overlapping section).

CARRY OUT THE PLAN

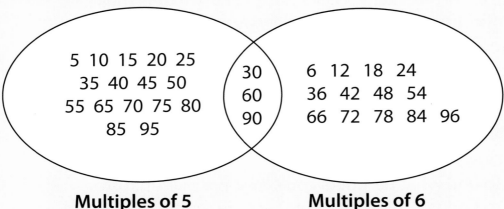

| **Multiples of 5** | **Multiples of 6** |

The numbers 30, 60, and 90 are multiples of both 5 and 6.

LOOK BACK

Go over the problem. Check that the question was answered. Make sure all numbers are two-digit numbers and that the multiples of 5 and the multiples of 6 are correct. Look for other ways to explain the solution. For example, from the answer you can see that the multiples of both 5 and 6 are also multiples of 30, which makes sense because $30 = 5 \times 6$.

ANSWER The numbers Nick could have on his uniform are 30, 60, or 90.

LEARN

Solve.

1. Sarah has some dog tags, each with a number from 1 through 30. She wants small dogs to have even-numbered tags. She wants dogs with curly hair to have tags with numbers that are multiples of 5. Which numbered tags could Sarah give to a small dog with curly hair?

    Explain your answer by using words and numbers, and show your answer by using a Venn diagram.

L E A R N

Explain Solutions to Problems

Show Multistep Solutions

> ## Worked Examples

You can use a table to solve a story problem and help explain the solution.

PROBLEM Roger received 5 silver dollars for his birthday. When he opened his coin box, he saw that he had twice as many quarters as he had silver dollars. When he put the quarters and silver dollars together, what was the value of all the coins?

SOLUTION

UNDERSTAND THE PROBLEM
You need to find how much money Roger has.
Facts you need: Roger has 5 silver dollars. He has twice as many quarters as silver dollars.

DEVISE A PLAN
Decide on a strategy.
- Make a table.
- Write a number sentence to find the total value.

Make the plan.
1. Make a table showing how many of each type of coin Roger has.

2. Find the value of all the coins of the same type (the total value of the quarters and the total value of the silver dollars).

3. Write a number sentence to add the total value of all the coins.

CARRY OUT THE PLAN

1 There are twice as many quarters as silver dollars, and there are 5 silver dollars, so there must be 10 quarters.

	Silver dollars	Quarters
Number	5	10

$5 \times \$1 = \$5$ $10 \times 25\text{¢} = 250\text{¢}$ or $\$2.50$

2 $\$5 + \$2.50 = \$7.50$

LOOK BACK

Go over the problem. Check that the question was answered. Make sure the table is correct, that you got the right number of quarters, and that you calculated the values correctly.

ANSWER Roger has $7.50.

Solve.

1. Wendy sorts and counts the coins in her piggy bank. She has 16 quarters. She has twice as many dimes as quarters. She has 20 pennies. She has half as many nickels as pennies. Does Wendy have enough money to buy a toy that costs $7.82? How do you know?

	Quarters	Dimes	Pennies	Nickels
Number	16			

LEARN

Explain Solutions to Problems

Express Solutions Clearly

Solve. Explain your answer.

1. Susie first put 3 quarters on the table. Then she put twice as many dimes as quarters on the table. How much money did Susie put on the table?

   Explain your answer.

Choose the option that best describes the solution to the problem.

2. Pete was driving to his grandmother's house 453 miles away. He drove 256 miles on Saturday and 147 miles on Sunday. How much farther does Pete have to drive?

   A. Add 256 and 147. Subtract this sum from 453. Pete has to drive another 50 miles.

   B. Add 256 and 147. Add this sum to 453. Pete has to drive another 856 miles.

   C. Add 256 and 147. Subtract this sum from 453. Pete has to drive another 344 miles.

3. Irene made $74 selling cookies and lemonade. She sold 14 cookies at $3 each. How much money did Irene make selling lemonade?

   A. Multiply 3 by 14. Subtract this product from 74. Irene made $32 selling lemonade.

   B. Multiply 3 by 14. Add this product to 74. Irene made $116 selling lemonade.

   C. Multiply 3 by 14. Subtract this product from 74. Irene made $23 selling lemonade.

TRY IT

4. Dennis bought 3 hamburgers, a drink, and an apple. Hamburgers cost $2 each, drinks cost $1.19, and apples cost $0.78. How much did Dennis spend?

   A. Multiply 2 by 3. Add 1.19 and 0.78 to the quotient. Dennis spent $7.97.

   B. Multiply 2 by 3. Add 1.19 and 0.78 to the product. Dennis spent $7.97.

   C. Multiply 2 by 3. Subtract 1.19 and 0.78 from the product. Dennis spent $4.03.

5. Sam sold 49 tickets on Monday. He sold 7 fewer tickets on Tuesday than on Monday. How many tickets did Sam sell both days combined?

   A. Subtract 7 from 49. Add this difference to 49. Sam sold 91 tickets on both days combined.

   B. Subtract 7 from 49. Add this difference to 49. Sam sold 42 tickets on both days combined.

   C. Subtract 7 from 49. Add this difference to 49. Sam sold 98 tickets on both days combined.

6. Seventy-five soccer players were at the camp. Five players left the camp. The rest were divided equally into teams of 7. How many teams were created?

   A. Add 5 and 75. Divide this difference by 5. Sixteen teams were created.

   B. Subtract 5 from 75. Divide this difference by 7. Seventy teams were created.

   C. Subtract 5 from 75. Divide this difference by 7. Ten teams were created.

TRY IT

Exact and Approximate Solutions

Rounded Answers

> ### Worked Examples

You can solve story problems and round the answer to a certain degree of accuracy, such as to the nearest ten, hundred, or thousand, or to the nearest dollar.

PROBLEM Ron bought 3 new baseball hats. If each hat cost $14.95, about how much did Ron spend? (Give your answer to the nearest dollar.)

SOLUTION

UNDERSTAND THE PROBLEM
You need to find how much Ron spent to the nearest dollar. **Facts you need:** Ron bought 3 new baseball hats. Each hat cost $14.95.

DEVISE A PLAN
Decide on a strategy.

- Write a number sentence.   • Make the plan

❶ Round the cost of each hat to the nearest dollar.

❷ Multiply 3 times the rounded cost of each hat.

CARRY OUT THE PLAN

❶ $14.95 rounded to the nearest dollar is $15.

❷ 3 × $15 = $45

LOOK BACK
Go over the problem. Check that the question was answered and the numbers were rounded correctly. Find the answer a different way. $15 + $15 + $15 = $45

ANSWER Ron spent about $45 on baseball hats.

Solve.

1. There were 5,892 people at the concert on Friday and 4,043 people at the concert on Saturday. About how many people attended the concert over the two days? (Give your answer to the nearest 1,000.)

2. Rosa has 347 songs on her MP3 player. Alexander has 182 songs on his player. About how many more songs does Rosa have? (Give your answer to the nearest 100.)

Read the problem. Tell whether an *exact* amount or an *approximate* amount is called for.

3. Serena buys a puzzle book for $5.67, a music book for $8.39, and a mystery book for $10.47. Should the cashier figure out the exact amount that Serena owes or an approximate amount? Explain.

4. Winnie has about 1 hour to play with a friend. She wants to play 3 different games. Should Winnie calculate an exact or approximate amount of time they should play each game? Explain.

5. Chef Max is making a cake. The recipe calls for 4 eggs, 5 cups of flour, and $2\frac{1}{2}$ cups of sugar. Should Chef Max measure the amounts exactly or approximately? Explain.

LEARN

Exact and Approximate Solutions

Accurate Solutions

Tell if the situation gives an *exact* amount or an *approximate* amount.

1. It takes about 15 minutes to drive to the store.

2. The plane arrives at 7:06 p.m.

Round to the nearest hundred.

3. 893

4. 3,562

5. 727

Round to the nearest dollar.

6. $1.28

7. $61.46

8. $452.71

Choose the answer.

9. Robyn bought a tree for $49.89, a shrub for $32.87, and a plant for $18.96. About how much did Robyn spend? (Give your answer to the nearest $10.)

   A. $80   B. $90   C. $100   D. $110

10. Tanya bought a book for $7.79, a postcard for $1.25, and a magazine for $3.35. About how much did Tanya spend? (Give your answer to the nearest dollar.)

    A. $11   B. $12   C. $13   D. $14

TRY IT

11. The computer factory made 6,236 computer chips one week.
Of these, 1,233 were faulty and had to be thrown away.
About how many computer chips were left over?
(Give your answer to the nearest 100 chips.)

    A. 5,300   B. 5,000

    C. 1,200   D. 500

12. The jet traveled 511 miles an hour for 4 hours.
About how many miles did the plane travel altogether?
(Give your answer to the nearest 100 miles.)

    A. 20,000 miles   B. 2,000 miles

    C. 1,000 miles   D. 500 miles

TRY IT

Check Accuracy of a Solution

Solve and Check

Worked Examples

You can use the problem-solving plan to solve story problems. You can check the accuracy of your answers.

PROBLEM A youth group collected used books to donate to a library, community center, and school. The youth group collected 4,290 books. The members noticed that 27 books had missing pages or were damaged. They recycled the damaged books and then separated the remaining books evenly among the 3 donation places. How many books did the youth group give to the community center?

SOLUTION

UNDERSTAND THE PROBLEM

You need to find how many books the group gave to the community center. **Facts you need:** The members collected 4,290 books; 27 of the books were damaged. The members divided the undamaged books evenly among 3 places.

DEVISE A PLAN

Decide on strategies.

- Use logical reasoning.
- Translate into a number sentence.

Make the plan.

1 Subtract 27 from 4,290 to find the number of undamaged books.

2 Divide that difference by 3 to find how many books the group gave to each donation place.

LEARN

CARRY OUT THE PLAN

1 $4,2\overset{81}{9}0$
  $-\ 27$
  $\overline{4,263}$

2 1,421 books
  $3\overline{)4,\!^{1}263}$

LOOK BACK

Go over the problem. Make sure you answered the question asked.
Make an estimate of the answer.

$4,290 - 30 = 4,260$ ⟶ Round 4,260 to a number that can be easily divided by 3. ⟶ $4,200 \div 3 = 1,400$

Compare the estimate to the answer. Is the answer reasonable?
Yes, 1,400 and 1,421 are close.
Check your work.

$1,421 \times 3 = 4,263$ $\qquad\qquad$ $1,463 + 27 = 1,490$

ANSWER The youth group gave 1,421 books to the community center.

Solve and check.

1. Mr. Reynolds set up 456 chairs for the concert in the park. He put the same number of chairs in each of 8 rows. How many chairs did Mr. Reynolds place in each row?

2. Shanna and her family went to an amusement park. They bought 5 tickets and ate lunch at the park. Each ticket cost $42.95. Lunch cost $52.00. How much did Shanna's family spend at the park?

LEARN

Check the answer.

3. Drew solved this problem and said the answer was 4,142 pairs of sunglasses.

   A store at the beach has 5,682 pairs of sunglasses in stock. The store sells 1,740 pairs of sunglasses. How many pairs of sunglasses does the store have now?

   Is Drew's answer correct? If not, what is the correct answer?

4. Lee solved this problem and said the answer was 390 miles.

   Mr. Gallo and his family are driving from their house to the beach. They have driven 218 miles and they have 172 miles left to go. How many total miles is it from their house to the beach?

   Is Lee's answer correct? If not, what is the correct answer?

5. Mr. Gallo spent 6 hours at the beach. He rented a beach chair and an umbrella while he was there. Beach chairs rent for $2.50 an hour, and umbrellas rent for $3.00 an hour.

   Tori said Mr. Gallo spent a total of $33.00 at the beach. Is Tori correct? Tell why or why not.

6. Jake, Marc, and Billy went to the arcade. They won 3,428 tickets. They used 2,000 tickets to get a toy rocket. They shared the remaining tickets equally.

   Fiona said each friend got 409 tickets. Is Fiona correct? Tell why or why not.

LEARN

Check Accuracy of a Solution

Look Back and Check

Solve.

1. A restaurant has 52 tables that each seat 4 people and 14 tables that each seat 8 people. Two hundred eighty-five people are sitting in the restaurant.

   Eric said there are 35 empty seats in the restaurant. Is Eric correct? Explain.

Choose the answer.

2. The sports club bought 8 new baseball bats for $320.

   Valerie said that each baseball bat cost $40. Which calculation can be used to check Valerie's answer?

   A. 40×8
      Valerie is not correct.

   B. $40 \div 320$
      Valerie is not correct.

   C. $40 \div 8$
      Valerie is not correct.

   D. 40×8
      Valerie is correct.

3. Candy had two coffee containers. One had 22 ounces of coffee and one had 34 ounces of coffee.

   Gino said Candy had a total of 12 ounces of coffee. Which statement is true?

   A. Gino is correct.

   B. Gino is not correct. Candy has a total of 56 ounces of coffee.

   C. Gino is not correct. Candy has a total of 112 ounces of coffee.

   D. Gino is not correct. Candy has a total of 748 ounces of coffee.

TRY IT

4. The animal park had 765 butterflies. It released 433 of the butterflies into the wild.

Nina said that the animal park now has 332 butterflies. Which statement is true?

A. Nina is correct.

B. Nina is not correct. The park has 1,198 butterflies.

C. Nina is not correct. The park has 1,100 butterflies.

D. Nina is not correct. The park has 432 butterflies.

5. Lauren solved this problem and said the answer was 6.

Yael made 24 ounces of pudding. She put the same amount of pudding into 6 cups. How much pudding was in each cup?

Is Lauren's answer correct? If not, what is the correct answer?

TRY IT

Find the Perimeter of Objects

Measure Perimeter

Worked Examples

You can use what you know about polygons to find the perimeter.

PROBLEM Find the perimeter of the square and rectangle.

4 cm

7 cm

5 cm

SOLUTION

PERIMETER OF THE SQUARE

1 Use what you know about squares to fill in the measure of all sides. Squares have 4 equal sides.

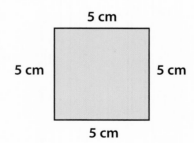

5 cm

5 cm

5 cm

5 cm

2 Add the length of all sides.

or

Multiply the length of one side by 4.

$P = 5 + 5 + 5 + 5$

$P = 20$

$P = 4 \times 5$

$P = 20$

L E A R N

PERIMETER OF THE RECTANGLE

1 Use what you know about rectangles
to fill in the measure of all sides.
Rectangles have opposite
sides equal.

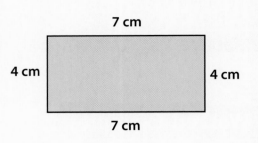

7 cm

4 cm   4 cm

7 cm

2 Add the length of all sides.

$P = 7 + 4 + 7 + 4$
$P = 22$

or

Multiply the length of the long
side by 2. Multiply the length of the
short side by 2. Add the two products.

$7 \times 2 = 14$
$4 \times 2 = 8$
$P = 14 + 8$
$P = 22$

ANSWER The perimeter of the square is 20 cm,
and the perimeter of the rectangle is 22 cm.

Find the perimeter.

1. $P = \underline{\ ?\ }$

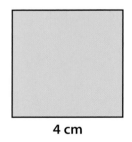

4 cm

2. $P = \underline{\ ?\ }$

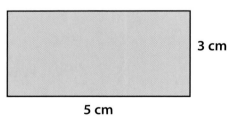

3 cm

5 cm

3. $P = \underline{\ ?\ }$

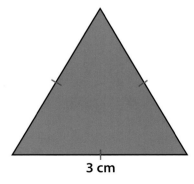

3 cm

4. $P = \underline{\ ?\ }$

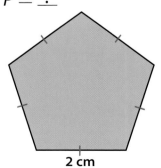

2 cm

LEARN

Find the Perimeter of Objects

Perimeter of Polygons

Find the perimeter.

1. $P = \underline{\ ?\ }$

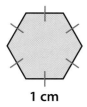

1 cm

2. $P = \underline{\ ?\ }$

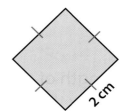

2 cm

3. $P = \underline{\ ?\ }$

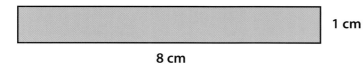

1 cm

8 cm

4. $P = \underline{\ ?\ }$

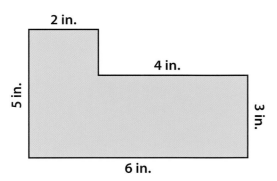

2 in.

4 in.

5 in.

3 in.

6 in.

5. $P = \underline{\ ?\ }$

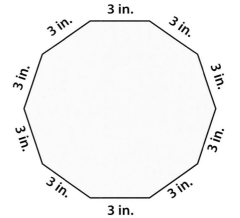

3 in.
3 in.
3 in.
3 in.
3 in.
3 in.
3 in.
3 in.
3 in.
3 in.

Choose the answer.

6. There are 64 squares on this game board. Each small square is 1 inch long. What is the perimeter of the game board?

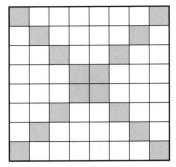

   A. 8 in.

   B. 16 in.

   C. 32 in.

   D. 64 in.

7. What is the perimeter of the triangle?

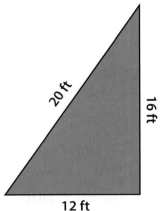

20 ft

16 ft

12 ft

   A. 32 ft

   B. 48 ft

   C. 96 ft

   D. 192 ft

8. This picture represents a playground that measures 6 m on each of its 6 sides. What is the perimeter of the playground?

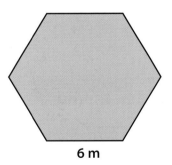

6 m

   A. 6 m

   B. 12 m

   B. 30 m

   D. 36 m

9. What is the perimeter of this shape?

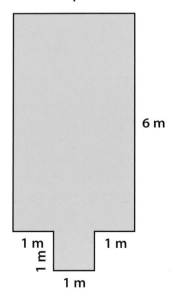

6 m

1 m

1 m

1 m

1 m

   A. 6 m

   B. 11 m

   C. 20 m

   D. 22 m

TRY IT

Rectangular Area

Grid-Paper Story Problems

Worked Examples

You can find the area of a shape by finding the length and width and finding how many square units fit inside the shape.

PROBLEM Charles is putting a vegetable garden in his yard. The picture shows where he plans to put his garden. What is the area of the garden?

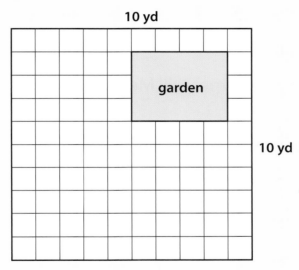

10 yd

garden

10 yd

SOLUTION

1 Count the squares along the long side of the garden to find that the width of the garden is 4 yards.

2 Count the squares along the short side of the garden to find that the length of the garden is 3 yards.

3 Use the length and the width to know that the garden covers 3 rows of 4 square yards, or $3 \times 4 = 12$.

ANSWER The area of the garden is 12 square yards.

L E A R N

Use this story problem to solve Problems 1–3.

Megan wants to carpet the floor of her tree house. The size of the floor is shown in the grid.

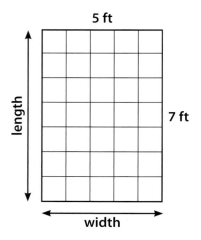

5 ft

length

7 ft

width

1. How many feet wide is the floor?

2. How many feet long is the floor?

3. How many square feet of carpet will Megan need?

Use this story problem to solve Problems 4 and 5.

Mrs. Parker wants to cover a tray with tiles. The tiles are each 1 inch square. The grid below shows the size of the tray.

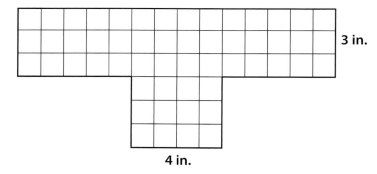

3 in.

4 in.

4. What is the area of each of the different rectangles?

5. How many tiles will Mrs. Parker need?

LEARN

Solve.

6. This picture shows where the couch is in Johnny's living room.

What is the area of the couch?

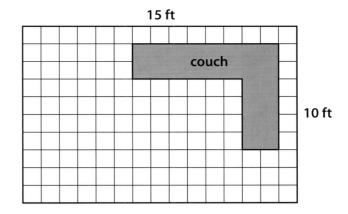

15 ft

couch

10 ft

7. Patrick has 32 concrete blocks to make a walkway. If he makes the walkway 4 blocks wide, how long can he make the walkway?

8. Quinn has 27 tiles to use on the wall behind her sink. She wants to put 9 tiles in each row. How many rows of tiles can she make?

LEARN

Rectangular Area

Area Story Problems

Use this story problem to solve Problems 1–3.

Mr. Jacoby wants to cover the playground shown here with rubber tiles. The rubber tiles are each 1 foot square.

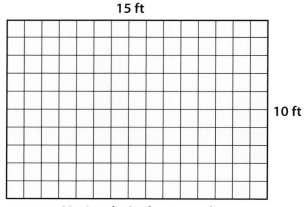

Mr. Jacoby's playground

1. How many squares wide is the playground (horizontally)?

2. How many squares long is the playground?

3. How many tiles will Mr. Jacoby need?

Solve.

4. Ron put a desk in his bedroom. The picture shows where he put the desk.

   What is the area of the desk?

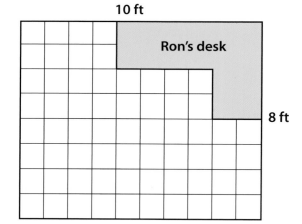

TRY IT

5. Gloria has 24 cork squares to make into a rectangular-shaped tack board. If she makes the board 6 squares wide, how long will the board be?

6. Seth used square patio blocks to make his patio. Each block was 1 foot long and 1 foot wide.

What is the area of Seth's patio?

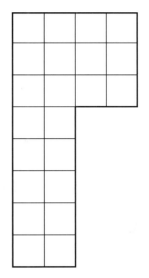

7. Aaron is making a rectangular patio in his yard. He has 36 square patio stones. Each stone is 1 foot by 1 foot. He wants to make his patio 9 feet long (or 9 stones long).

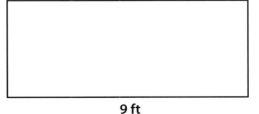

9 ft

How wide can he make his patio if he wants to use all his stones?

8. Kenta wanted to arrange 20 stickers into a rectangular shape. Each sticker was 1 inch long and 1 inch wide. He wanted to put 5 stickers in each row so the rectangle would be 5 inches long.

How wide would his rectangle be?

T R Y   I T

9. Yolanda wanted to arrange 45 stickers into a rectangular shape. Each sticker was 1 inch long and 1 inch wide. She wanted to put 5 stickers in each row so the rectangle would be 5 inches long.

   How wide would her rectangle be?

Choose the answer.

10. Judy visited a flower garden.

    What is the area of the flower garden?

    A. 4 sq ft

    B. 8 sq ft

    C. 16 sq ft

    D. 60 sq ft

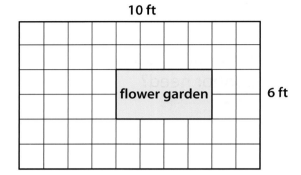

10 ft

flower garden

6 ft

11. These figures all have a perimeter of 16 inches. Which one has an area of 16 square inches?

    A.

    B.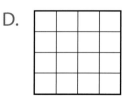

    C.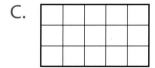

    D.

TRY IT

How Many Squares Does It Take?

Cover the Solid

Solve.

1. Connor wants to completely cover this rectangular prism using square tiles.

How many square tiles does Connor need?

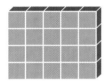

2. Josh wants to completely cover this rectangular prism using square tiles.

How many square tiles does Josh need?

3. Clancy wants to completely cover this rectangular prism using square tiles.

How many square tiles does Clancy need?

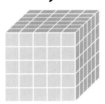

4. Find the number of square units it takes to cover this solid.

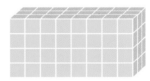

Choose the answer.

5. About how many squares would cover this cube?

A. about 50

B. about 150

C. about 200

D. about 300

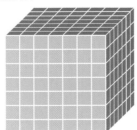

6. About how many squares would cover this rectangular prism?

A. about 10

B. about 100

C. about 150

D. about 200

T R Y   I T

How Many Cubes Does It Take?

Measure Volume

Find the volume.

1.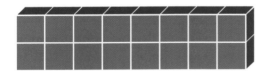

2.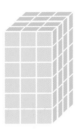

Solve.

3. Jack stacked these cubes.
How many cubes did he use?

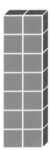

4. Look at how Allison stacked her cubes.

How many cubes did she use?

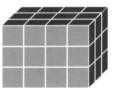

Choose the answer.

5. The picture at right shows 1 cube.

John used the cubes to build the shape below.

How many cubes are in the shape John built?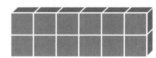

A. 24

B. 20

C. 14

D. 12

TRY IT

6. The picture at right shows 1 cube.

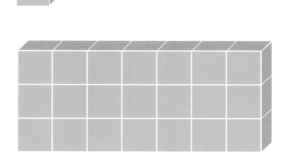

Laura built the wall with the cubes.

How many cubes did Laura use to build the wall?

A. 7   B. 14

C. 21   D. 28

7. Marcus is using blocks to make a cube. If each cube is solid and has no holes, how many blocks did Marcus use?

A. 16   B. 48

C. 64   D. 96

8. What is the volume in cubic centimeters of the figure shown at right?

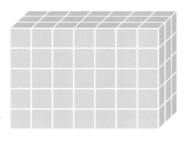

A. 15 cm³

B. 21 cm³

C. 35 cm³

D. 105 cm³

= 1 cubic centimeter

9. Matilda is filling a box with 1-inch sugar cubes. She filled the bottom with one layer as shown in the picture at right.

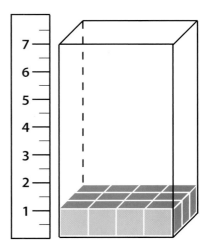

When she completely fills the box, how many sugar cubes will be in the box?

A. 12   B. 19

C. 84   D. 133

TRY IT

10. About how many cubes were used to make this figure?

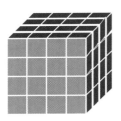

A. 45   B. 60

C. 90   D. 120

11. About how many cubes were used to make this figure?

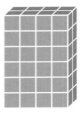

A. 50   B. 30

C. 20   D. 10

12. Which rectangular prism has a volume closest to 100 cubic units?

A.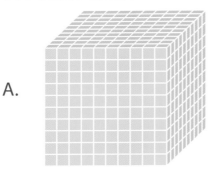

B.

C.

13. Which cube has a volume closest to 30 cubic units?

A.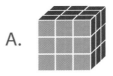

B.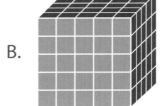

C.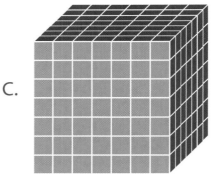

Solve.

14. Debbie is filling a box with 1-inch cubes. She filled the bottom layer as shown at right.

Debbie wants to completely fill the box. Including the cubes Debbie has already put in the box, how many cubes wil she use in all?

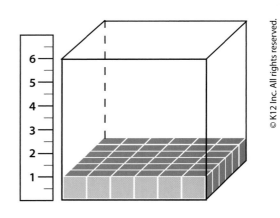

T R Y   I T